MAN AND BEAST

MAN AND BEAST

by R. A. MARCHANT

The Macmillan Company
New York

Library of Congress catalog card number: 68-21304

Printed in the United States of America

FIRST PRINTING

PICTURE CREDITS: Beth Bergman 17, 33, 79, 147; Culver Pictures,
Inc., 85; Historical Pictures Service—Chicago, 6-7, 10, 38, 46, 55, 112,
115; NASA, 107; Phoenix (Arizona) Zoo, 91; Picture Collection—New
York Public Library, 24, 72, 163; Radio Times Hulton Picture Library,
xiv, 51, 58-59, 66,69, 101; South African Tourist Corporation, title page,
124, 138-139, 144; The Zoological Society of London, 154. Picture research
by Sally Raymond.

Title page photo: Group of springbok, Kruger National Park

*To My Parents
and My Parents-in-Law*

PREFACE

*

THERE ARE so many articles and books written nowadays to publicize the causes of animal welfare and conservation that it might appear that man has at last accepted his responsibilities to the rest of creation. Unfortunately, this is still not really true. If it were, there would be no need for the continual flow of propaganda, nor for the efforts of the numerous animal protection societies.

Nevertheless, the general attitude today is a great improvement on what it was even fifty years ago, and it is at last beginning to be accepted that conservation is not merely the concern of well-meaning cranks but is something vital to man's future welfare. Every wild animal population occupies a special niche in world ecology and represents an irreplaceable storehouse of scientific knowledge. It is, therefore, essential that no species should be allowed to die out if it can possibly be saved.

It has taken a remarkably long time for man to realize that his fate is so closely linked with that of the rest of the animal kingdom. Ever since he first domesticated animals and invented farming, he has tended to regard himself as something set apart from all other forms of life, which, it was thought, existed only for his benefit. Because of this, animals were denied all rights and dignities. They might be hunted or exploited in any way which ingenuity suggested, and the most merciless treatment was thought justifiable if some man profited from what was done.

In the course of such exploitation many animal populations were relentlessly pursued and persecuted for the sake of their skins, or some other commercially valuable attribute, and others were taken into service to work or to fight for or to amuse their masters. The predators, the birds and animals that preyed on the creatures that man wished to exploit, became regarded as deadly enemies. Their slaughter was often made to appear justified by interpreting animal behavior according to human moral values, so that a creature that killed became regarded as a murderer and its execution became a social virtue.

Even when a growing social conscience led to campaigns against cruelty to animals, few people suggested that the new spirit of compassion should be extended to the predators. Indeed, once it became accepted that areas of wilderness should be set aside for the preservation of wild animals, the massacre of the predators was frequently regarded as essential to the success of the schemes. The "big bad wolf" and the animals like it were seen as the cruelly ravenous enemies of the creatures man admired. It has taken a great deal of zoological research and hard, practical experience to drive home the lesson that this attitude is unjustified and that it is nonsense to apply provocative terms such as bloodthirsty or vicious or treacherous to animal behavior.

This is something that has still not been fully taken in by the man in the street. He will laugh at the medieval notion of convening special courts to try animals for their crimes, but he continues to interpret animal behavior in human terms, and in terms dictated by sentiment rather than reason. The scientist is now well aware that the so-called law of the jungle is not the savage anarchy of popular imagination but a carefully ordered system in which each species, whatever its habits, is biologically necessary.

The close investigation of animal behavior, both in the laboratory and under natural conditions, has produced surprises and has caused many old ideas to be scrapped or drastically revised. It is no longer possible to regard animals either as living machines, operating solely by instinct, or as near humans, lacking only the gift of speech.

Indeed, even the ability to communicate is not unique to man, and it has become clear that some animals and insects are much more efficient in this direction than was previously thought possible. It may even be that an age-old dream will eventually come true and that man will be able to enter into genuine communication with another animal species. Research is at present being conducted into the possibility of talking to dolphins, and if this project proves successful, it will undoubtedly lead to the most dramatic development yet in man's constantly changing attitude to other animals.

CONTENTS

*

MAN AND BEAST

The use of war dogs dates back
four thousand years; a medieval Irish
manuscript shows one in full armor.

CHAPTER 1

IN THE BEGINNING

*

IN THE BEGINNING men were as animals and animals as men. That is what the folklore of the Micmac Indians says, and it probably gives a true enough picture of what things were like many thousands of years ago when men were only just starting to be recognizable as such. The lives of those incredibly remote ancestors of ours were uncomplicated and unrefined by inventions and imaginations. Their wants—of food, shelter and mates—were the same as those of the animals that surrounded them, and their way of satisfying them was just as direct; what they wanted they took, when they were strong enough.

Fortunately for the development of civilization, man is not a particularly strong animal, nor is he especially fleet of foot. In order to stay alive and to catch his food, he was therefore forced to make use of his latent ability to think and plan. This led to the invention of the first crude tools and weapons and, eventually, to all the comforts and amenities of modern life.

For a very long time, however, man had no reason to

suppose himself to be in any way distinct from the rest of the animal creation. He could certainly have had no feeling of superiority. It was obvious to him, just as it is to the hunting communities that have survived into modern times, that many of the other animals were much better equipped by nature. They were stronger and faster than he was and must sometimes have seemed as superior mentally as they were physically.

Because of this, those early men would have had a respect for other forms of life. This does not mean that they were sentimental about animals, or even that they liked them. The conditions under which they lived did not allow for such emotions. To them animals were simply creatures either to be hunted or avoided according to their natures. Some beasts might be hated and feared, but there could be none of the casualness that was to be shown later by men used to animals that could be tamed and herded. Earliest man was always too conscious that animals not only provided him with his food but were all too likely to be the cause of his death.

In many cases the degree of respect that this inspired was elaborated into reverence, and eventually various forms of animal worship came into being. This sort of religion had a world-wide spread and lasted well into historical times. Indeed, it still exists today, and traces of it are even to be found in the beliefs of people who imagine themselves to be far removed from such primitive ideas.

It has been suggested that the enormously increased difficulties faced by hunters during the Ice Ages were largely responsible for the appearance of a special god of hunting. In the milder climate of earlier days a great deal of plant food could be gathered and game was abundant. When the ice sheets spread over much of the land, the plants disappeared and the animals became fewer. Consequently, anything that might help in the chase was seized upon, and so the god of the hunt was invented and all sorts of magical practices were begun. The hunters, or their tribal magicians, put on animal masks and imitated their prey in ritual dances and movements in order to transfer to themselves the powers of strength, speed or cunning that they envied. In many cases they thought that they actually became the animal they imitated.

This transfer of identities was possible because of the acceptance, general in primitive people, that everything in nature was equally alive and thus basically alike. All things possessed a soul, and so rocks, trees, animals and human beings differed only in the outward form that each assumed.

At death the soul moved into a new body, and this added another complication to the lives of the early men, for it meant that the business of the hunt was not ended with the killing. This had to be followed by certain rites to ensure that the soul of the slain beast would not harbor animosity against its killers and that it would retain all it needed for its subsequent rebirth.

Many examples of this attitude have been observed in surviving races of hunters. The Alaskan Eskimos threw the entrails of fish back into the water, for otherwise the soul of the fish died and the species was not replenished. The Lapps were obeying the same impulse when they put fish scales and bones on a stone to be taken under the protection of the fish god. The heads, feet and wings of birds were treated in the same way to ensure a plentiful supply for the future.

Eskimos also believed that because seals and whales lived in the sea they were unable to drink and so suffered from a continual and intolerable thirst. They therefore allowed themselves to be caught, knowing that the Eskimos would end their agony by giving them an offering of fresh water. If a hunter neglected to put this water into the mouth of his victim, the other seals or whales would know of his treachery and would never again allow themselves to be caught by him.

Polar bears were envious of men's possessions and so their skins had to be hung up in the house alongside the tools they coveted—knives and bow drills if the animal was male and needles and skin scrapers for a female. The soul of the animal stayed in the skin until it was driven out in a special ceremony four or five days later. It then departed, taking with it the spirits of the proffered tools.

Another idea that gained almost universal acceptance was that the desirable qualities of animals—their strength, speed or cunning—would be passed on to the man who ate their flesh. The same idea lay behind some of the rituals of the old hunter-magicians when they invented sorcery to help them to overcome their difficulties. Thus the heart and blood of a beast of prey became especially highly valued as a source of courage. Other creatures were thought to impart strength, speed or cunning, according to their natures. When conditions became easier, these ideas resulted in a more selective hunting policy, for bad qualities were as easily transmitted as good and so no hunter would think of eating animals with undesirable attributes. Some tribes avoided members of the cattle family because they did not wish to become dull and heavy, and other animals were despised on account of the cowardice they imparted. The Chiriguano tribe of eastern Bolivia carried this belief to such lengths that they refused to eat the vicuña for fear they might develop woolly skins.

Although belief in this sort of sympathetic magic is so

:neral, it was probably never quite so important to early
an as the rituals already described, in which the tribal
gicians assumed the nature of animals through imitative
ances and the wearing of masks and skins. This idea that
)wer could be obtained over animals by imitating them led
ectly to the idea that the soul, whether of animal or man,
uld be controlled by any sort of likeness, acted or drawn,
:f the body in which it was living. This is the reason for the
dislike, reported by so many explorers, that some races had
of being photographed; it also explains the belief that
sticking pins into a wax effigy could injure the person
represented. To the Ice Age hunter the theory offered the
chance of ensuring a successful hunt by first killing the image
of the animal that was to be his prey.

Many of the cave paintings that have survived from
prehistoric times must have been used in magic rituals to
ensure good hunting. The mere possibility that these might
work would be enough for people leading such precarious
lives as primitive bushmen or the hunters of prehistory. The
latter certainly needed all the help that rituals and sorcerers
could give when, with their ineffective-seeming weapons,
they faced such dangerous beasts as the rhinoceros and the
mammoth.

It used to be thought that these animals would have been
too powerful for them to tackle, but archaeologists have found
that necessity frequently forced them to attempt the feat,
and large numbers of these animals were slain. In order to
understand how this could have been accomplished, the
historians turned to anthropology and studied the hunting
methods still used today, or until very recently, by primitive
tribes. It soon became clear that man is ingenious enough
and, in cases of need, brave enough to compensate for any

Early men soon learned to hunt together to obtain meat.

deficiencies of his weapons. Pygmies had no hesitation in attacking elephants even though they were armed with nothing but spears and bush knives, and their method could easily be the same as that used by prehistoric man against the mammoth.

As a preliminary to the attack they covered themselves with elephant dung, in order to disguise their scent and make it easy to approach their prey. When they came within striking distance, they thrust their spears into the soft underparts of the animal and then followed it at a safe distance until it collapsed. Its end would then be hastened by hacking off its trunk so that it bled to death.

It is also likely that the less risky techniques of driving animals into a swamp or of surrounding them with a ring of fire were well understood by Stone Age hunters. Both methods remained popular in Africa because of their simplicity and frightening effectiveness. When a ring of fire was used, dry grass was set alight so that the elephants were surrounded by the flames, and when they attempted to break

out, already terrified, they were driven back by an uproar of shouts and drummings. They then soon succumbed to the heat and the smoke or were so weakened that they could easily be slaughtered.

A communal hunt is the most effective means of obtaining a good supply of meat, and this was probably a lesson that man learned very early in his history.

One of the simplest of such cooperative techniques was that practiced by the Tasmanians. They made a huge circle, so big that the individual members of it were only just within shouting distance of each other, and at a given signal moved forward, shouting and making as much noise as possible. By this means the game was frightened and was gradually driven into a more and more confined space until the ring of hunters became so constricted that those forming it were able to link hands. Then the spears were thrown and the clubs wielded until the scene became a chaos of blood, screams and bellows as the confused, panic-stricken animals were butchered.

The South African bushmen also used this type of hunting, but in a more elaborate form which required careful preparation. A valley was selected, and across it a fence was built. Gaps were left here and there, but with large pitfalls dug out of them and with hunters concealed near by. The rest of the tribe moved out in a wide circle to beat the game in toward the fence. On reaching it, the animals would run along until they found a gap, but when they tried to pass through, they fell into the pits and could be slaughtered at the hunters' leisure.

Later on, when man had progressed a little from the food-gathering stage, hunting ceased to be an economic necessity and became instead either a means of proving manhood or a mere leisure-time amusement. The solitary hunter who set out after a dangerous beast to prove his own courage and skill probably had little lasting effect on animal populations. It was a case of one man against one beast and either of the two might emerge the victor. The sportsman-hunter is a different proposition, however. Throughout history he has shown himself to be every bit as lacking in restraint as his remote ancestors, and without the same excuse of necessity. The more such hunters have been able to kill, the better they have been pleased and the louder have been their boasts. Ancient monarchs erected monuments to commemorate their hunting exploits, and nineteenth century sportsmen published detailed lists of the numbers and sizes of the animals they slaughtered. Some such lists make staggering reading. One Indian army officer accounted for close to 320 caribou in a single day's hunting. Equally enormous scores were quite common.

No creature was safe from the hunters, and in North America the birds suffered particularly. In Omaha it was considered a very poor day's sport that did not provide a man with a great heaped-up wagonload of plover and other birds. It more often happened that the wagon was filled too quickly, in which case its load of dead and dying birds was dumped on the prairie and the gallant hunter blazed away again into the flocks in order to refill it.

The magnitude of the slaughter in North America during the last century is almost unbelievable. The buffalo, counted in millions at the beginning of the century, was only just saved from extinction, and the passenger pigeon, single flocks of which outnumbered the entire bird population of the

*Unrestricted slaughter has led to
the extinction of many species.*

British Isles, was wiped off the face of the earth. Nor was the attack limited to America. The other continents suffered almost as drastically.

Fortunately, most people eventually realized the irresponsibility of this sort of behavior and so unrestricted killing is no longer typical of the sportsman. Indeed, it is probably fair to say that over the past fifty or sixty years many of the hunters have shown a far keener and more genuine interest in wildlife study and conservation than have some of their detractors, whose animal horizons are frequently limited to dogs, cats and budgerigars.

It was a long time, though, before the idea of conservation gained even partial acceptance. The final disappearance of the game has always seemed too remote to worry about, and so until very recently the one aim of the hunter remained the same as that of very early man, namely, to improve his weapons and his techniques so that his kills might be greater. To this end elaborate traps have been devised, but one of the most significant improvements came thousands of years ago when the dog was tamed and taken into service as a hunting assistant.

Exactly how this happened is not known, but it has been suggested that the first dogs were scavengers and became friends of man as a result of hanging about his settlements in search of food. Although there were very few men about in those early days—it has been estimated that the winter population of Britain in paleolithic times did not exceed two or three thousand—the stench from their kitchen middens would have drawn the dogs from far away.

Although he perhaps resented them at first, it would not have been long before man realized that these camp followers had their uses. They took little or nothing that was of value to him, but disposed of what was often offensive rubbish and gave noisy warning of the approach of both man and beast.

Some authorities consider that these dogs became accustomed to receiving the entrails of the game killed by the hunters and so very soon developed a keen interest in the hunt itself. Eventually, instead of following the hunters, they took to running ahead of them, seeking out the game and joining in the attack.

All this, however, is very hypothetical. It may be that in the earliest days the dogs that hung about man's encampments were themselves regarded as a source of meat or skins or that they were originally tamed as beasts of burden, to drag man's belongings from place to place. It is even possible that this was the first use made of all domesticated animals, even of those members of the deer family that have been tamed. It is certainly a fact that reindeer have been used to pull sledges since very ancient times, but whether or not they were domesticated for the purpose is debatable. So also is the date of domestication. One scientist, Henn Pohlhausen, thinks this might be as early as about 12,000 B.C., and if correct, it makes the reindeer the first animal, apart from the dog, to enter man's service. There was quite a long gap before they were joined by any others. Naturally, only the most approximate dates can be given, but it is known that the inhabitants of Jericho, in Jordan, owned domesticated goats as long ago as 6000 or 7000 B.C.

Cattle were not tamed until about two thousand years after this, and by that time the possibilities of the pig had also been realized. The domestication of the latter animal could not be attempted until man had learned to live in settled communities, for it is a notoriously difficult creature to drive and the feat would probably have been beyond the powers of the early nomads. Incidentally, this has been suggested as one reason why the pig, so highly valued by many people, is in some parts of the world regarded as unclean. The nomads despised the people who lived settled lives, and by a process of association the feeling was carried over to the pig that frequently shared their homes. The attitude became so deeply engrained that even when the nomads abandoned their wandering life, pork remained a prohibited food.

No precise dates are possible for the domestication of the horse, but it is known that it must have been tamed well before 2000 B.C., for that was when migrating armies in horse-drawn chariots started to sweep across the Middle East, to the great terror of the original inhabitants. It was a long time, however, before anyone thought, or dared, to mount it.

In those early days there must have been attempts to domesticate unsuitable species, and at one time it almost looked as if the giant sloth, a huge creature standing about fifteen feet high, had once been considered a possible candidate. Remains found in a South American cave suggested that these animals had been stabled there and killed by the Indians as and when required. The domestication theory was favored because fodder had obviously been cut by man and fed to the beasts. Later investigations caused this belief to be modified, and eventually most of the experts came to the conclusion that the sloths had not been bred in the cave but merely kept alive for a while after they had been trapped.

It is quite possible that it was by means of such trappings in caves and gullies that some of the genuine domestications were begun. It is noteworthy, too, that such a procedure bears a close resemblance to the method employed with elephants today. These are sometimes bred in captivity, but the supply is also maintained by the periodic capture of adult wild beasts in keddahs, or stockades. Because of this, the elephant is sometimes left off the list of the world's domesticated animals, despite the many uses to which it is put.

Altogether, there are only sixteen mammals of agricultural significance that qualify for inclusion on the list of domesticated animals: reindeer, pig, horse, ass, cow, zebu, buffalo, yak, gayal, banteng, sheep, goat, llama, alpaca, dromedary and camel. Despite its brevity the list represents one of man's greatest triumphs, but unfortunately the success it represents has had a disastrous effect on the attitude to animals in general.

Previously man had felt a kinship with the rest of nature and had a natural respect for other forms of life. Prolonged association with tamed animals changed this completely. It engendered a contempt for them and led to the belief that man was a superior being for whose especial benefit all other animals had been created. These were denied all dignity and rights, and those that did not contribute directly to man's comfort remained only on sufferance and provided they did not interfere with his arrangements. The ones that did interfere, the crop robbers and the predators that occasionally raided the domestic herds, were regarded as out-and-out enemies. Merciless war was declared against them.

CHAPTER 2

WAR AGAINST ENEMIES

THIS WAR has continued nonstop to the present day, and countless generations of farmers and agriculturists have insisted that animals can be divided into two sorts, those that are useful and those that are harmful. Many nature lovers have also accepted this idea, but have fought fiercely to have particular creatures removed from the harmful to the useful category.

This is especially true of bird lovers who thought careful investigations would remove slurs cast on some birds by proving that any attacks they might make on crops and gardens were amply compensated by the destruction of insect pests. It was argued that many birds were condemned because the damage they do is immediately evident, whereas their good works remain invisible. These friends of the birds spoke loudly of the astronomical numbers of caterpillars and the like eaten during the year and of thousands of tons of wireworm destroyed, but fruit growers and farmers countered by pointing to stripped orchards and ruined crops, and continued to keep shotguns handy.

Meanwhile the naturalists tried, and are still trying, to make everyone see that generally speaking not enough is known of all the factors involved to justify any black or white verdict. This is only possible in a case such as that of the so-called locust birds. These congregate in enormous numbers wherever there is a sufficient supply of the food they find attractive and are obvious enemies of the farmers. The wood pigeon is the chief offender in Britain, but its ravages fade beside those of the vast colonies of birds to be found in some parts of North America and Africa. The biggest, and therefore most dangerous roosts, are those of the red-billed quelca, an African bird. There might be as many as twenty million in a single colony, all feeding on crops that are vitally important if parts of Africa are to be kept free of starvation.

Apart from such cases as this, it becomes more and more difficult as knowledge increases to talk in terms of menace or benefit. Even the most elaborate of investigations, such as the wartime study of the effect of rooks on agriculture, can do little more than produce a mass of statistics, the evaluation of which is extremely difficult. Those with decided views pick out the figures that suit their arguments and hurl them at their opponents.

A further complication arises because animals and birds are not nearly so mechanical in their behavior as many of the older natural history books might suggest. It has become increasingly evident that individuals of the same species can vary widely in their likes and dislikes. Even when a species is judged to be generally harmless, or even beneficial, there is frequently the odd rogue to be found among its numbers. When the little owl was investigated and largely cleared of the attacks made on it, some of these rogues were found. They customarily destroyed game, and so as individuals fully deserved the strictures made on the species as a whole.

Eagles are among the predators most threatened by man.

About the only certainty to emerge from all the conflicting evidence is that the full details of how the lives of different species, including man, interlock are still not understood. But if the experts confess uncertainty, the man in the street, or perhaps it should be garden, continues to work by the rule of inherited prejudice. Any bird habitually seen near growing crops or fruit is dubbed a thief, and birds of prey are not tolerated where it is hoped to rear young pheasants or other game birds.

The excessive protection that sporting interests have afforded some species at the expense of others has had a disastrous effect on wildlife in many parts of the world. All predators, the flesh-eaters that live on other birds or animals, have in the past been labeled vermin and have been ruthlessly attacked. Of the birds, eagles have suffered especially from this attitude, among them the American bald eagle. It is only fair to say that there is no single or simple reason that fully explains the bald eagle's decline, but the effect of man's enmity is clearly demonstrated by available figures.

In Alaska, for example, there was for a long time a price on the eagle's head, and between 1917 and 1952 this bounty was paid out on no fewer than 100,000 of the birds. Such a sustained attack must have a disastrous effect on the bird population. Nowadays it is estimated that there are less than 4,000 bald eagles in the entire United States. One of the first grants made by the World Wildlife Fund in the United States was of $8,500 to assist the National Audubon Society expand its five-year survey of the distribution and status of the species. A really disturbing factor regarding the bald eagles is the low percentage of nesting successes of the surviving birds.

Sometimes the policy of trying to protect sporting interests by killing off the "vermin" has provided dramatic illustrations of the dangers resulting from upsetting the delicate natural balance between species. Where the predators have been slaughtered almost to the point of extinction, rats and mice have multiplied alarmingly. Rodents are capable of explosive increases in population when the control system breaks down, and when their numbers reach plague proportions, they do an incalculable amount of damage.

It was the relentless persecution of predators that was at least partly responsible for the great Scottish vole plague of the 1870s and 1890s. A thousand square miles of sheep-rearing country was so severely affected that fodder had to be imported to keep the sheep alive. Even so, the lamb crop was much reduced and the financial effects were serious.

Many countries can provide similar examples of how the persecution of a creature regarded as a nuisance has had unexpected and unwelcome results. The early settlers in Australia did not like the noisy kookaburra bird and shot it on sight. They stopped doing this only when it was realized that the bird fed on snakes and that its disappearance was followed by a rapid increase in these even more objectionable neighbors. Elsewhere in the tropics a too zealous campaign against snakes has sometimes proved unwise. Only a minority of these maligned creatures is dangerous, and many of them do valuable work in keeping down the numbers of rats. So when an area is cleared of snakes, it is liable to be plagued by rodents.

One onslaught on a predator had world-wide economic consequences. This was when ranchers in the United States were waging an intensive war against coyotes. These animals were detested because of attacks on lambs and calves, but as the wild dogs decreased, so the rabbits, ground squirrels and mice flourished. Rabbits might seem preferable to coyotes but, as the Australian sheep farmers had already discovered, they can prove a greater menace than any number of predators. In Australia millions of pounds had to be spent on rabbit control and thousands of miles of rabbit-proof fencing was erected. Even then victory was a long way from sight before myxomatosis thinned out the hordes. The jack rabbit of the western United States is not quite the same animal as the familiar bunny, and it did not get quite so out of hand. Even so, before the increased numbers were brought under control, so much damage was done to the ranges that it looked as if the price of meat would have to rise.

Nevertheless, where animal populations build up to such an extent that man's activities are seriously threatened, it is obvious that some offensive measures must be taken. Again, where it looks as if disease might be spread, wiping

out the offenders becomes a matter of self-defense. Because
of this, action was at one time necessary against gophers,
or ground squirrels, in California because it was found that
they were carrying the germs of bubonic plague. Rats, too,
have always played a prominent part in the spreading of
this terrible disease, and their germ-carrying is one of the
principal reasons why not even the most sentimental and
militant of animal lovers can dispute that they should be
regarded as enemies.

No such argument, however, can be brought forward to
support the harsh treatment meted out to many other animals,
including such species as badgers and otters. Both of these
are responsible for a certain amount of damage, but to nothing
like the degree of which they are accused. It is only the
occasional rogue badger that concentrates on poultry and
game birds, and recent research suggests that the fisherman
has little reason to fear the otter. A pair of these animals
in a salmon or trout stream will thin out the fish, but it has
been plausibly argued that, because of the consequent increase
in the available food supply, those that are left grow bigger
and so the weight of the fisherman's catch remains much
the same.

In March 1965 the Fauna Preservation Society called a
conference on British predators, and it was generally agreed
by the naturalists, foresters, agriculturists and sportsmen
represented that there was a strong case for protecting the
badger. In any case, factors other than the purely economic
ones should be considered with such creatures as the badger
and the otter. The British countryside would be an infinitely
poorer place without them.

The point that some wild animals have a social value that
outweighs the damage they might do was emphasized in
1964 by the Leopold Report on Predator and Rodent Control

in the United States. As the report put it, "For every person whose sheep may be molested by a coyote, there are perhaps a thousand others who would thrill to hear a coyote chorus." Fortunately, this report was heeded, and in 1965 the United States Government announced the adoption of a new attitude toward predator control based on "the husbandry of all wildlife"; the numbers of animals killed would be the minimum required to meet the needs of an area.

One of the animals that might benefit from this change of heart is the cougar, which at the moment is barely holding its own. There are very few left in the eastern United States, and in 1965 it was estimated that there were only about four thousand left in the western states. Early settlers told hair-raising stories of the cougar's ferocity, but such yarns had little basis in fact and may even have been inspired by nothing more than the animal's lively curiosity regarding man and his activities. On balance the cougar should probably be regarded as beneficial, since it serves as a check on the increase of deer that eat and damage crops.

With the larger predators, however, it is easier to understand the generally destructive attitude, for many of these are big enough and dangerous enough to inspire fear. The movement to preserve wildlife is a very worthy one, and it would be sad indeed if such magnificent beasts as lions and tigers ever became totally extinct in the wild, but it must be admitted that distance probably lends enchantment to the view. There is a lot of difference in a lion thousands of miles away and one at the bottom of the garden. The impression left by some books is that all wild beasts are really cuddly pets at heart, but this is just as misleading as the pictures, painted in earlier accounts, of ravening monsters perpetually athirst for blood.

Large wild beasts are the most uncomfortable of neighbors,

a continual threat to domestic animals and an occasional one to man himself. In Kenya rhinos kill several human beings and hundreds of domestic animals every year, so it is not surprising that they are heartily feared and detested. It is understandable that man should not want these or similar beasts in the areas in which he lives. In the past there was plenty of wilderness where they could remain undisturbed save by the big-game hunters, but the ever-increasing demand for agricultural land means that these areas are shrinking rapidly. In the United States bears have been pushed back steadily ever since the first settlers arrived, and they are now threatened even in Alaska, their last stronghold. Conservationists and cattle ranchers clashed there in the summer of 1964 when, because of reported serious cattle losses on Kodiak Island, a plane equipped with an automatic rifle was used to kill any of the gigantic bears found in the grazing area. "Civilization is moving north," one of the ranchers was reported to have said, "and the bear is going to have to give way." Despite all the efforts of conservationists to prove it wrong, this prophecy will probably be fulfilled. After all, even in some of the national parks, set up in part to protect such animals, the bears are now regarded by some as a threat to the safety of vacationers. It may well be that there will soon be no room to spare for genuine "wild" animals of the larger sorts.

This situation was reached long ago in Britain, where the wolf and the bear, the only two native species that could be considered harmful to man, were exterminated hundreds of years ago. Of these two, the wolf was always much more numerous than the bear and remained a pest long after the latter had become a vague, almost mythical monster. It is generally accepted that the last British wolf was not killed until 1786. In Saxon times the animal had become such a menace that special roadside refuges were built so that travelers attacked by it could flee to safety.

In some European countries wolves are still dangerous. There are frequent, well-authenticated accounts of attacks by them, and in February 1963 one Italian couple was besieged by wolves for eighteen days and eventually had to be rescued by a squad of armed police.

All this suggests that Old World wolves are much fiercer than their North American cousins. There are plenty of stories of attacks by these, but George G. Goodwin, associate curator of mammals at the American Museum of Natural History, has declared that in North America no wolf has ever made an unprovoked attack on human beings. This sounds strange in view of the wolf's reputation for savagery, but the United States Fish and Wildlife Service has investigated all accounts of supposed attacks in recent years and has not found one that withstands inquiry.

Some authorities on animal behavior also doubt the allegation that wounded wolves are eaten by other members of the pack. The German scientist Konrad Lorenz insists that wolves have to learn to cooperate with each other and so are inhibited against killing a fellow pack member. His observations suggest that fights between wolves end when the beaten animal voluntarily exposes its throat to the slash of the other's fangs. This is accepted as surrender and the fatal blow is not struck.

Despite all this uncertainty about the real nature of wolves, it remains indisputably true that they are expensive and worrying neighbors. Even when there is plenty of food for them in the wild, ranchers always have to guard against the possibility of attacks on domestic herds. When they deliberately turn their attention to the farmers' flocks and

"Broncos and Timber Wolves," by Frederic Remington; domestic herds are the wolf's favorite target.

herds, either because these are more easily available or because of a shortage of other food, they can do an enormous amount of damage.

At the end of the nineteenth and at the beginning of the twentieth century they were costing the United States millions of dollars every year, and it took a tremendous effort to bring them under control. In Wyoming it was estimated that wolves were costing the ranchers four times as much as was needed to run the state government, and in 1897 a New Mexican rancher blamed them for the loss of five hundred head of livestock every year.

Obviously, this could not be tolerated, and the war that was subsequently waged against them was economically necessary. Some phases of the conflict were not very economically conducted, however. Heavy reliance was placed on the bounty system, which has a long history but little else to recommend it. Bounties offer plenty of scope for fraud, and many a dog or coyote or even a rabbit ear earned a reward, since those who made the payments seldom peered too closely into a sack of stinking remains.

Even when it is not complicated by dishonesty, the bounty system remains an expensive way of removing a pest. This was emphasized by the figures produced as long ago as 1886 by Dr. G. Hart Merriam. He reported that over a period of eighteen months the State of Pennsylvania had paid out $92,000 in bounties on vermin that did less than $2,000 worth of damage. However, despite all the drawbacks the system has always been widely used and will probably continue to be so for a long time to come.

In England a great variety of animals, from hedgehogs to foxes, have had prices put on their heads at various times, and in Scotland in 1621 Thomas Gordon earned himself £13 13/4 by killing one of the country's few remaining wolves. This price compares very favorably with the penny per wolf that was offered by the Massachusetts Bay Company in 1630. In New Jersey in 1697 the reward was a little more worth while, varying from 10 shillings to a pound. The lower amount was paid to Indians and Negroes and the other to white men, which seems to have been carrying color distinctions to extravagant lengths.

Apart from its obvious weaknesses, the bounty system is rarely completely successful in ridding an area of predators. The last few animals tend to possess such cunning and caution that even the promise of really high rewards does not always make the effort worth while for bounty hunters. In America some of the lingering outlaw wolves became nationally famous, and their exploits make fantastic reading.

One of the best known was an animal nicknamed Dakota

Three Toes, which had its hunting grounds in Harding County, South Dakota, from about 1910 to 1925. Incredible as it sounds, the ravages of this one animal may have been partly the reason why Harding County was one of the few areas in the United States where the population decreased between 1910 and 1920. This was because of the enormous losses he caused. In one three-month spasm of ferocity he killed $6,700 worth of stock, despite the expensive "predator-proof" fencing with which the animals were protected. He was adept at singling out the prize animal of a group, and when the desperate ranchers at last managed to poison his mate in 1920, he revenged her by destroying a herd of breeding cows on one ranch and every one of thirty-four valuable imported sheep on a neighboring spread.

These were merely highlights of years of unstoppable slaughter. Penned sheep and cattle were in constant danger and sometimes the wolf and his mate would stampede a herd over the edge of a cliff in order, so it seemed, to cause as much loss as possible. In the winter they drove the animals into natural traps in the snow-filled gullies and then butchered them at their leisure.

All the efforts of the ranchers and of the hunters who had been tempted by the offered $500 bounty to kill or capture Three Toes were countered with ease. Attempts to poison him were hopeless because, unlike most wolves, he ate only from his own kills and never touched carrion. He was equally superior to traps. These fascinated but did not deceive him. Indeed, he had great fun digging them up and playing with them and was even reported to have learned to spring them with sticks or stones. In 1923 the ranchers decided that he was too wily for them or the professional wolf hunters they had employed, and so they applied for government help. They estimated that by then he had cost them a minimum of $50,000. The actual figure may well have been much higher, and his career was still by no means over.

The first effort of the government predator control agency was an ignominious failure. The hunter sent to Harding County spent a few days finding out just what he would be up against and then left, without setting a trap or following a single trail. His replacement was more enterprising. He spent eight months on the job, during which time he killed twenty-two coyotes with his poisoned baits but never tempted Three Toes to a bite.

The following year, after a six-week spell of activity during which Three Toes destroyed $4000 worth of stock, the ranchers again petitioned the United States Biological Survey. This time the nation's most experienced wolf hunter, Clyde F. Briggs, was sent in, and Three Toes, his senses blunted a little, perhaps, by age, found that at last he had met his match. Undeterred by the scornful comments of the locals, Briggs announced, after a preliminary survey, that he would rely on traps. Before setting these, he buried them for a week or more in a pile of manure, and when he dug them out, he knelt on a wolfskin, wore wolfskin gloves and moccasins and carried them to his chosen locations in a wolfskin bag.

Three Toes was apparently still not deceived, but Briggs was not downhearted even when he found one of the traps dug up and made harmless. He moved the sprung trap to a fresh site, transplanted a small bush to hide it and hoped for rain. It came that very night, and the next morning when he rode out to inspect the trap, Three Toes, the savage killer that had rampaged over the country for so many years, lay docilely across the uprooted bush. His curiosity had got the better of him.

Having been defeated, he accepted the situation and made no effort to attack the trapper. Briggs tied him up and tried

to take him in his car to Buffalo, the state capital, but Three
Toes was spared the ignominy of being exhibited in captivity.
He died before the car had gone more than three or four
miles, and a subsequent autopsy declared his death to be due to
old age. The timing was dramatic but the cause of death came
as no surprise, since Three Toes must have been about twenty
years old and wolves are normally considered aged at ten or
just over.

Such an incredibly destructive animal obviously had to be
dealt with, but elsewhere there have been reminders that
even wolves are a part of nature's scheme of things and that
to destroy them can be unwise. At one time there was a
ferocious campaign waged against them in the far north in
order to protect the caribou. When so many had been killed
that the caribou were able to expand almost unchecked,
everyone was pleased. Unfortunately, the supplies of lichen
that was the food of the caribou did not expand with the
herds. More and more animals were trying to feed off less
and less lichen, and the condition of the caribou deteriorated
alarmingly. Eventually great numbers died, and the ones
left were for a long time in very poor condition.

It was then realized that not only had the wolves been a
population check but, by killing mostly the aged and the
ailing among the caribou, they had ensured that only the
more vigorous animals survived and bred. Fortunately not
all the wolves had been killed, and gradually the natural
balance was to some extent restored. In many other cases,
however, the regrets have come too late.

CHAPTER 3

COMMERCIAL EXPLOITATION

ALTHOUGH IT IS to be regretted, the ruthless attitude toward creatures that threaten man's domestic animals or his livelihood can be understood. What is amazing, however, is that a combination of greed and shortsightedness has often prompted an equally bloodthirsty attitude toward animals that are economically valuable. This is especially so with the fur-bearing animals, and for a very long time no one appeared to see the folly of the policy of wholesale slaughter that threatened numerous species with extinction, thus killing the geese that laid the golden eggs.

The number of animals killed in order to satisfy this universal desire for fur must run into a great many millions. Numerous species have been involved, but one that has suffered particularly is the beaver. For a long time the chief use of its pelt was in hatmaking, and the association between the animal and the trade was so close that in Chaucer's day the words "bever" and hat were almost synonymous.

A sixteenth century writer remarked rather sourly that

these hats were brought from overseas along with a lot of other vanities, and it is most likely that their country of origin was France, where the hatmakers of La Rochelle were famous. It was they who provided the incentive for much of the early exploration of North America, for they found that the beaver fur to be obtained there meant a tremendous increase in their trade. By the end of the sixteenth century beaver felt had again become the overwhelmingly dominant material of the hatmaker, a position from which shortage of pelts had once threatened to remove it, and was to remain unchallenged until the middle of the nineteenth century.

The wealth of furs in North America became not only the spur to the exploration of the continent but also a cause of rivalry and war between nations. Dutch, French, English and Indians were all involved in the struggle, and the Europeans fought each other fiercely through the warring tribes of Iroquois and Hurons.

After 1670 the Hudson's Bay Company came into the picture, and a fabulous wealth of furs passed through the hands of the company's factors. There were sable and ermine, mink and silver fox, but whatever the fur, it was all measured against the value of the beaver. No money changed hands between the Indian trappers and the traders. Instead, the furs were purchased with counters, valued at a quarter, a half or a whole beaver skin, and then these counters were exchanged for the beads, blankets and guns that the Indians chose. Eventually the beaver population fell alarmingly, and if the requirements of the hatters had not dropped in the second half of the nineteenth century, the animal would probably have become extinct.

Unlikely as it sounds, none of this slaughter was caused by the demand for fur coats. All the skins were used either for hats or for trimmings, as the fur coat itself did not then exist. Cave men had covered themselves with furs and Indians were known to wear coats of beaver pelts, but it was not until quite late in the nineteenth century that the idea of the fur coat was discovered by civilization.

The fact that men's hats thus nearly caused the death of a species is usually not nearly so emphasized as is the whole-sale slaughter of birds to satisfy the whims of women's millinery fashions. Perhaps this was because felt hats were not obviously of animal origin, whereas it was evident to the dullest intelligence that a great many birds must have died in order to provide the feathers that bedecked the extravagant concoctions on women's heads.

This was especially so in the many cases where it was not merely the plumage but the actual bird that was so used. In 1886 Dr. Frank Chapman made a personal spot check on the hats that he saw during a stroll in New York and reported that out of 700, no fewer than 542 were decorated with the mounted heads of birds. In the same year American ornithologists, who were campaigning against the destruction of birds by the millinery trade, published a bulletin stating that in America alone more than five million birds were being killed annually.

This mania for plumage and mounted birds raged from about 1870 onward, and it was about this same time that the world of fashion became really conscious of the possibilities of fur. A fur coat became a costly necessity in the wardrobe of every woman of standing. This, of course, intensified the already severe exploitation of the fur-bearing animals.

Among those that suffered onslaughts were the northern fur seal and the sea otter. Early explorers of the Siberian

Arctic and Alaska, and the grim Bering Straits that separate the two continents, had discovered enormous herds of these animals, and from the mid-eighteenth century onward the Russians carried on a lucrative trade in their oil and leather. This was a bloodthirsty period in Alaskan history. The fur traders were greedy and frequently vicious men who terrorized and enslaved the Aleuts and other natives. It is said of one of these men, named Pushkareff, that some of the natives whom he had forced to work for him jumped into the sea and drowned themselves rather than endure his cruelties, and that soon afterward, in a fit of temper, he threw the others in after them.

As the numbers of otters and seals were depleted, fur traders pushed deeper into the unknown, and in 1786 Gerasim Pribylov found the tiny islands that were to prove the answer to a sealer's prayer. They contained the long-sought-after breeding places of the fur seals and the beaches were crowded with hundreds of thousands of the valuable animals, more than any of the sealers had ever seen in one place before. From that moment the great slaughter began.

This was accelerated when in 1796 Thomas Chapman, who was buying sealskins at 3 halfpence each and using them to cover traveling trunks, developed a method of removing the stiff guard hairs, thus making the soft under-fur usable. This widened the market for the product and sent the price rocketing. At one stage the cost of a sealskin reached as much as 32 shillings and the fur was used first for men's hats and waistcoats and eventually for full-length coats.

At last the Russians realized they were recklessly destroying a valuable and irreplaceable asset, and an era of more intelligent management began. Thanks to this the number of seals in the herds began to build up again, but when

The popularity of exotic furs may bring about the extinction of such big cats as the leopard and the cheetah.

Russia sold Alaska to the United States in 1867, another period of uncontrolled exploitation was under way.

This continued until 1911, when the United States Government took over the management of the breeding grounds. Carefully controlled exploitation halted the terrible drop in population, and nowadays the Pribilof herd is regarded as a fine example of wildlife management. There is a steady population of about 1,500,000 seals and between 60,000 and 70,000 skins are taken each year. This harvesting has no cumulative effect on the herd since the victims are mostly the surplus males.

The whole process is so strictly and scientifically controlled that it could almost be regarded as a form of fur farming. This enterprise began to take shape toward the end of the nineteenth century, when it became obvious that although the demand for furs was going to continue, it was only too likely that the supply of animals would dwindle and disappear. The first attempts to rear fur-bearing animals in captivity were made in Canada. There were a few minkeries as early as 1866, but the first of the projects to gain real popularity was the farming of silver foxes. This had been carried on quietly in Prince Edward Island from 1894 onward, but the high prices paid at the London fur auctions in the early years of the twentieth century stimulated a boom. Fox farms mushroomed and the price of breeding stock rocketed from $3000 in 1910 to as much as $35,000 in 1913.

Since then fur farming has become a well established industry in many countries, and a great variety of creatures, from mink to rabbits, are now bred for their fur. The most interesting of them all, however, is probably the chinchilla. The fur of these small South American rodents has always been prized for its extreme beauty, but in the earlier years of this century it looked as if chinchilla fur was soon to become only a memory. The animals had become so scarce that trappers declared it to be no longer worth their while to hunt them. As the price of each pelt had by then risen to $56, it can be seen that they must have become very scarce indeed.

Unfortunately, chinchilla farms seemed out of the question because none of the animals had survived attempts to move them from the great height of their homes in the Andes. However, after the First World War Matthias Chapman, ignoring the experts who assured him that the attempt was futile, determined to make another effort to capture some of these extremely valuable animals and start a chinchilla farm in California.

He managed to capture a dozen but was then faced with the apparently insuperable problem of moving them. This he eventually solved by the exercise of extreme patience and considerable ingenuity. For two years after their capture he kept the animals in the Andes at an altitude of 11,000 feet. They were then carefully moved down to 9,000 feet, where they were kept for a year. Further well-spaced moves were then made down the mountains until, nearly six years after their capture, the chinchillas were at sea level and ready for the long journey to Los Angeles. To help them survive the tropical heat encountered on this voyage, they were put in a cage containing a hundred-pound block of ice. The cage was also surrounded by canvas which was kept continually moist. Mr. and Mrs. Chapman watched over their charges day and night and frequently had to revive them with cold douches when it seemed as if they were going to succumb to the heat. This unremitting care was successful, and the chinchillas reached their new home safely and in good health. Mr. and Mrs. Chapman, and the world's furriers and naturalists, were delighted, and a new and valuable type of fur farming began.

Fur farming is sometimes attacked as being "cruel," but conservationists find it infinitely preferable to the wholesale slaughter of wild animals for the sake of their pelts and skins. Many animal populations have been and still are seriously endangered by this activity. The high price paid for python skins has made killing these snakes such a profitable business, despite the protection given them by the law, that they may be extinct in South Africa within a few years. In the United States alligators are similarly under relentless attack because of the demand for their skins by the manufacturers of expensive shoes and handbags, and it was recently considered necessary for the Department of the Interior to seek an amendment to the criminal code in order to afford the species more protection.

The most spectacular assault by the fashion conscious, though, is on the big cats—leopards and cheetahs. In 1964 it was announced that 50,000 leopard skins, all but about 500 of them obtained illegally, were being exported each year from East Africa. A campaign was launched to discourage the fashions that financed this slaughter, but progress has been slow. A member of the Fauna Preservation Society told one American lady about the situation and she replied that since it seemed that leopards might shortly become extinct, she would buy two coats while they were still available. Nor was this an isolated reaction, for when the editor of *Vogue* was asked to cease publicizing leopard-skin coats and accessories, she agreed to do so but said she would not tell her readers the reason, as the knowledge that leopards were becoming scarce would be an added inducement to some women to own such a coat.

As well as being responsible for the destruction of so many fur-bearing animals, fashion must also bear part of the blame for the sad decline of the whale. This animal was formerly present in large numbers in most of the seas of the world, but some species have been so relentlessly hunted over so many years that naturalists are prophesying their imminent extinction. Of course, this is not solely the fault of fashion, for whales have been commercially important for a number of reasons and are still hunted and harried despite fashion's loss of interest in them.

Nevertheless, the dictates of fashion caused the deaths of many thousands of the animals because whalebone was for centuries the mainstay of the corset-making industry. This substance is not really bone at all. Its correct name is baleen and it is a horny growth in the mouths of some varieties of whales, serving to trap the crustacea on which they feed. Its earliest decorative use was probably to fasten the helmet plumes of the knights of the Middle Ages. It was not long, however, before their ladies realized it was an ideal material for molding and disciplining their figures to the new shapes fashion demanded as the centuries wore on, and once the discovery was made, a period of more relentless pursuit began for the whales.

By the end of the nineteenth century whalebone had risen to a peak price of $5,600 a ton, and the value of the blubber was an additional incentive. Fabulous profits were being made, and the sole thought of the whalers was to kill as many animals as possible before the bottom fell out of the market. This eventually happened about the turn of the century when the manufacturers of women's clothes found cheap substitutes for baleen, and at the same time the development of the gas and electricity industries ended the demand for whale oil, which had formerly lit the cities of the world. The whaling industry then declined to such an extent that the whale, by that time a dangerously diminished species, began very slowly to increase its numbers.

Unfortunately, the recovery did not last very long. Ingenious scientists soon found a way of converting whale oil to fats, and so whaling again became a profitable occupation. In fact, modern science has made hunting the whale more attractive commercially than ever, for nowadays hardly any part of the animal fails to yield a profit. The liver, which might weigh as much as a ton, surrenders an oil superior to that produced by cod, and the various glands provide a number of drugs and vitamins. The flesh and blubber is cut up and boiled to render it down to oil, which can then be treated for use in the manufacture of a wide range of products. Margarine can be made from whale oil and so can soap, cosmetics

*Over the centuries whalers have relentlessly hunted
the whale for its blubber and other products.*

and lubricants, and it also plays a part in the manufacture of
textiles, paints and varnishes. The amount of oil extracted
from a whale is enormous, and it has been said that a season's
output of one factory ship would make enough margarine
to keep a million people supplied for a year. Nor is all this
the end of the whale's usefulness. The entrails and the very
bones are valuable, for they can both be powdered and then
used for cattle fodder and manure. It is ironical that almost
the only part of the whale that is no longer in demand is the
previously much prized baleen. This is so little used nowadays
that it is sometimes thrown away, the only part of the animal
to be so carelessly treated.

Despite the discarding of baleen by the world of fashion, the whale still has a part to play in the closely related sphere of perfumery. This it does by virtue of the strange substance known as ambergris, which is, perhaps, the most fabulous and mysterious of all animal products. Some species of whales habitually eat squid and shellfish, and the horny beaks and shells of these sometimes set up severe irritation in their stomachs. A jellylike substance then forms round the source of the trouble, and when it is eventually excreted, it becomes the ambergris of commerce.

Before this process was understood, it was thought that ambergris was gum exuded by the roots of trees, and that is why it was given the name "gray amber." The strangeness of its supposed origin and its scarcity ensured a high price for it during the Middle Ages, when it was used to cure epilepsy and to add flavor to food and wine. Its widespread use in perfumery did not begin until the nineteenth century, and it then acquired a legendary value and became the subject of sailors' yarns and daydreams. An inhabitant of St. Helena is reputed to have discovered on the beach there a piece weighing nearly 400 pounds and worth $56,000, and some Norwegians once killed a sperm whale containing a piece worth $75,600.

Unlike many of the other animal substances that are used in the manufacture of perfumes, ambergris, or its essential odoriferous element, has never been successfully duplicated in the laboratory. Because the others can be synthesized, animals now play a much less important role than was previously the case.

What is perhaps the most fascinating chapter in the story of the connection between animals and perfume deals with a failure. This was the attempt by a man named Hedenstrom to market a perfume made from the marrow of long-dead mammoths. He was in exile, but because of his education and abilities he was put in charge in 1809 of the survey of the recently discovered New Siberian Islands. These were rich in mammoth remains, and so he conceived a great idea for an entirely new cosmetic, went so far as to choose the name Pommade à Mammoth for the finished product, and collected great quantities of bones for its manufacture. Unfortunately, on his way back to civilization he was unwise enough to take these into a house with him and the heat thawed them so that the marrow melted and was lost. This evidently discouraged him, for although he returned to New Siberia the following year, he made no further attempt to collect mammoth marrow.

At the time of this unlucky venture the mammoths of Siberia were commercially important as a valuable source of ivory. Arab traders were buying and selling mammoth tusks as early as the tenth century, and nine hundred years later about fifty thousand pounds of this ivory was being sold annually at the market in Yakutsk.

Despite this wealth from the north, the conventional source of ivory has naturally always been the elephant of the south, and the value placed upon its tusks is one of the principal reasons for the African elephant having become so depleted. Ivory has been esteemed for its use in art and ornamentation since prehistoric times.

Ancient peoples used it lavishly, even if not quite on the same scale as the Africans who, according to Pliny, even built fences and cattle stalls of ivory. Solomon had a throne made of ivory, and in Greece and Rome it was a much favored material among sculptors. During the Middle Ages ivory carving was a feature of religious art and, because of its own beauty and because of the way in which it could be decorated, it was also widely used in the making of caskets and trinkets.

Ivory is still valuable, but plastics are now often used in its place, and this is true also of tortoise shell, another animal product formerly very highly prized for its decorative effect. Many people express regrets when a natural product is replaced by an artificial one, but all should be pleased that the demand for tortoise shell has lessened since obtaining it involved a great deal of cruelty. It used to be common practice to strip the individual plates off the turtle's body by suspending it, alive, over a fire until the heat peeled them off. Any unfortunate turtles that survived this torture were then flung back into the sea in the mistaken belief that a fresh layer of shell would grow.

Man's determination not to miss any chance of profit when dealing with wild creatures is clearly demonstrated in the history of the great auk. This flightless bird nested in great numbers on coastal and island rocks in the North Atlantic and was formerly persecuted because it was so rich in oil. At one time boiling the birds in huge vats was quite an industry on the Funk Islands. There were no trees growing on these bleak rocks, but there were so many birds that the pots were kept boiling by the use of their bodies as fuel. Although their original numbers were so vast, it is not surprising that this prodigal usage rapidly diminished them until they became very nearly extinct.

Even then they were not left in peace. Once they could be considered rare birds they became prized as specimens for museums and private collections, and the last two great auks were killed in June 1844 by Icelandic boatmen who received £9 for the two skins.

Today man considers himself to be more enlightened, and a revival of the plan once put forward to boil up penguins to make soap grease would provoke an outburst of protest. Nevertheless, in many ways animals are just as mercilessly exploited as ever, and it takes more than indignation to stop something that is showing a profit. Factory farming provides a recent example. Its critics claim that animals are treated as mere meat-producing machines and are reared under unnatural and inhumane conditions. Most people, however, give more thought to the price of meat in the shops than to the lives led by farm animals, and the campaign against factory farms does not really seem to be achieving much apart from a good press coverage.

The uproar over factory farming would probably fade into comparative insignificance beside the one there would be if the suggested possible use of animals as factory workers was ever put into practice. This might seem an unlikely thing to happen in these days of increased automation, but there are still many jobs that cannot be performed by machines and many others for which machines could be designed but which animals could perhaps do more cheaply.

An Australian farmer has been reported to be using a chimpanzee to muster cattle, round up sheep and clean fleeces, and American scientists have trained pigeons to check transistors and to inspect drug capsules for imperfections. Public opinion would probably prevent any enterprising manufacturing chemist using the birds in this way, but it has been demonstrated that it is within their capabilities.

Some of the workers involved in the testing and training of the animals argue that if an animal is cheaper than a machine, then it is only logical to use the animal. Against this, many people believe that the idea of using animals as slaves in this way is basically wrong. To them it seems a reversion to the days when animals were thought to have been created solely to serve man and that he was entitled to exploit them in any way he pleased.

Nevertheless, the idea is really only an extension of the already accepted use of animals. Provided the load is not too heavy and the animal is well treated, nobody protests at the thought of a horse having to pull a cart. The only difference between this and a pigeon pecking at a key to reject a defective pill or a monkey operating a punch press is that one concept is familiar whereas the other is new and strange. It cannot even be argued that the new ideas would have pigeons and monkeys behaving in ways that were unnatural to them for, after all, no horse teaches itself to pull a cart.

CHAPTER 4

ANIMALS AT WORK AND WAR

*

Man has always been quick to see new ways to make use of the animals he has tamed and domesticated. The chief service that has been demanded, however, has been transport, first for his goods and then for himself. There is probably no fairly large animal that man has domesticated, or tried to domesticate, that has not at some time been put between the shafts of a cart. Even pigs have been used in this way.

The principal draft and transport animals, though, are the familiar horses and members of the cattle family, and of these cattle were at first the more important. Teams of plow oxen survived in England until the present century, and in parts of the world cattle, particularly the buffalo, are still extensively used to pull carts, work in the rice fields and raise water from the wells. They were being used for these or similar purposes long before the horse was similarly trained, and in the very early days of animal domestication they were even hitched to war chariots.

These were, of course, far removed from the light mobile

weapons that they were to become. In fact, they were probably little more than supply carts. Not only were the oxen too slow for much else, but the carts themselves were at first very clumsily constructed. A five-thousand-year-old war chariot depicted on the ancient "standard of Ur" has solid wooden wheels and could not have been much of a threat to nimble foot soldiers. Nevertheless it represents the beginnings of mechanized warfare and was the forerunner of vehicles that were to change history.

The full story of the development of the chariot is not very clear because it all happened too long ago. It is known, however, that it was the Hittites who perfected it as a weapon of war over a thousand years before the birth of Christ. Their horse-drawn chariots had spoked wheels and combined high speed with great maneuverability. Each one carried two warriors in addition to the driver, and this striking power, added to their other advantages, made them well-nigh unbeatable.

This type of chariot was a decisive factor in the battle of Kadesh, fought between the Egyptians and the Hittites in 1296 B.C. Both sides had war chariots, but the Egyptian models carried only one warrior and proved to be nothing like so effective as those of their opponents. When these hurtled into the attack, in a terrifying confusion of dust, rattling wheels, drumming hoof beats and shrieking men, and preceded by a ceaseless rain of arrows, much of the Egyptian army gave way and scattered in a panic-stricken rout.

Chariots were in use long before horses were ridden, and the most convincing explanation of this is that the first horses to be domesticated were very small and so were unsuitable for use as mounts.

With the evolution of a sturdy enough breed and the mastery of the new art, the pattern of history changed com-

Horse-drawn chariots were developed by the
Hittites as a weapon of war around 1000 B.C.
and used for triumphal processions as well.

pletely. The nomads of Asia, who lived and died on their
horses, eating their flesh and drinking the milk of the mares,
proved vastly superior to the armies of civilized countries and
for many long centuries were able to raid and ravage almost
at will. Cavalry remained the most effective of all weapons
right up to very modern times. It even maintained a place in
the world's armies long after mechanical progress had made
not only horse-drawn transport but even the farm horse very
largely obsolete. When the Second World War began in
1939, many of the armies involved still contained large cavalry
contingents.

Animals generally have played a much larger part in
modern warfare than is sometimes realized. Plaques on the
R.S.P.C.A. War Memorial Dispensary at Kilburn, in London,
record that 484,143 animals were killed by enemy action or

died as a result of disease or accident during the Great War of 1914–18. In France alone 725,216 sick or wounded creatures were treated in the R.S.P.C.A. veterinary centers.

In that war, cavalry was still being used in large numbers, and in addition to horses, army mules and other draft animals had a vital part to play. The Allies also followed the German lead in the use of dogs, which proved especially valuable in carrying messages to and from advance units. Not only could they move much faster than a man on foot and negotiate obstacles he might find impassable, but being smaller, they were much less likely to be hit than a human courier. Lacking trained dogs but realizing their uses, the U.S. Army borrowed numbers of them from the French and the British.

The numbers of animals involved in the Second World War were not so large. The variety, however, was probably greater. As well as the horses already mentioned, many thousands of mules were called up for military service, and so were numerous elephants and camels. These beasts were enormously valuable in the Asian campaigns. Camels hauled supplies to U.S. Army bases in India, and elephants solved many transport and construction problems in difficult country. American signal construction crews even used them as convenient moving platforms from which to service telephone lines. The necessary road and bridge building in the Burma campaign would have been much more difficult, if not impossible, had it not been for the work of the powerful elephants and their oozies, or handlers. Water buffalo and other pack cattle were also used extensively in the Pacific and Asian campaigns. There and in Italy, the pack animals could often get through when mechanized transport became hopelessly bogged down.

Dogs, too, proved that they retained their value even in

the most mechanized of wars. This time the U.S. Army
trained its own, making use of the expertise of naturalized
citizens who had been dog specialists in various European
armies during the First World War. It has been said that as
many as 125,000 American dogs were recruited for war
service. They were used not only for patrol and message
carrying duties but also for mine-detecting and for dragging
telephone wires to the front line or wherever they were needed.
This saved members of the Signal Corps from some dangerous
trips under fire. Another invaluable use of dogs was in locat-
ing and rescuing the wounded, and in order to carry out this
task they were often dropped by parachute with the stretcher
bearers of airborne divisions.

The military history of the dog dates back at least to the
time of Hammurabi, who ruled over Babylon about four
thousand years ago. His soldiers are known to have gone into
battle accompanied by large war dogs, and it is probable that
other armies of that time did likewise. The Roman author
Pliny (A.D. 23–79) mentions the use of dogs in war, and the
memorial column of the Emperor Marcus Aurelius (A.D.
121–180) shows dogs dressed in armor. During the Middle
Ages they even wore headpieces and crests, and examples
of these medieval suits of armor are to be found in several
museums.

Elizabeth I is reputed to have presented a hundred dogs
to the Earl of Essex to be used in his Irish campaign, but
after this war dogs dropped out of favor for some reason.
They were sometimes used in the West Indies in operations
against runaway slaves, and a few did good service on sentry
duty in the Boer War, but they did not officially reappear in
British forces in any real numbers until halfway through
World War I. Their reintroduction, long resisted by the more

orthodox, was then inspired by the successful exploitation of war dogs by the Germans, who had started their first army dog school as early as 1848.

The Germans were also the pioneers of guide dogs for the blind and of police dogs. They set up a training center for guide dogs at Potsdam just after the First World War, hoping to be able to provide "seeing eyes" for their war-blinded veterans. This came to the notice of Mrs. Dorothy Eustis, an American who was particularly interested in breeding and training German shepherds. She and her husband were so impressed that they started a similar establishment in Switzerland, where they lived. During the 1930s the idea spread from Switzerland to the other European countries and to the United States.

The relationship between a trained guide dog and its handler is probably about as close as is possible between an animal and a man, and it is remarkable that a dog can be so successfully accustomed to a pattern of behavior that is in many ways unnatural for it. This triumph of training over instinct makes the guide dog every bit as noteworthy as the sheepdog, which is usually presented as the star performer among working animals. It is true that the training of sheepdogs has been so refined upon that a really good dog is capable of almost incredible feats. Nevertheless, a basic part of his skill is the result of instinct rather than training. His ancestors, the wolves, were accustomed to herding the animals on which they preyed and were as adept as he is at cutting out one animal from the mass. The breeding and training of the dog has developed and improved this natural ability.

Using dogs as guards or for police work is also making use of their natural attributes, and they have been valued as guards ever since they started associating with man.

Alsatians, or German shepherd dogs, and Doberman pin-schers are the breeds most often used in this sort of work, but some police forces also still value the bloodhound. This dog was probably introduced into Great Britain by William the Conqueror, and over the nine hundred years since then a mass of legend and exaggeration has gathered around it. So many stories have featured the menacing baying of bloodhounds hot on the trail of some unfortunate fugitive that it has become accepted as one of the most spine-chilling of animal sounds. In face, the dogs that were used in America and elsewhere to attack escaped convicts and runaway slaves were crossbred animals, especially trained for that work. The true bloodhound is one of the gentlest of creatures. Its name has nothing to do with supposed ferocity, but is a reminder that it was considered to be blooded, that is, to be pure bred and of aristocratic ancestry.

The use of dogs as draft animals has a history as long as, and possibly even longer than, their use as guards. It is especially associated with the Arctic regions, where the Eskimos have for thousands of years used huskies to draw their sledges, and even in this mechanized age these dogs, and others related to them, retain much of their old importance. They provide transport over country that would otherwise be impassable and in conditions that are often all but impossible. The strange thing is that this usage arouses little protest, despite the known harshness of the dogs' lives, whereas the continental practice of hitching them to light trade carts is often condemned as cruel.

Dog-drawn carts are illegal in Britain now, but for a good part of the nineteenth century they were quite popular, especially in the south of England. It has been suggested that they first became used as a means of avoiding the payment

The pig is rival to the dog as a truffle hunter.

of tolls, since dogs and goats were originally omitted from the list of draft animals for which these were demanded. Be that as it may, the fish sellers of Brighton and the other south coast towns favored them for making deliveries to inland customers. The carts they used were about the size of a boy's gocart of today, but the seat was sometimes extended to make room for a second passenger. The number of dogs in harness depended on the owner's whims and fancies, but was generally between two and six.

Pulling fish carts over the Sussex Downs is not the only job that dogs have lost in recent times. The turnspit dog has vanished entirely. This dog was found in large kitchens up to the nineteenth century. It was a small, long-bodied animal that was put in a wheel attached to the spit; as the dog ran, the spit turned and the joint roasted. If the dog proved laggard, it was encouraged by having red hot coals placed in the bottom of the wheel. As it climbed away from them, the wheel revolved. When roasting jacks came into general use, the turnspit dog ceased to be needed and the very breed died out. Similarly, the improvement of rural water supplies means that dogs are no longer needed to tread a wheel or walk a circle in order to draw water from the wells.

The spread of modern ideas of comfort and convenience also makes it doubtful if anyone anywhere still needs to press dogs into service as pillows or footwarmers. Nor would anyone nowadays expect one to behave as a living candelabra. The very idea of this seems absurd and even impossible, but in ancient China small dogs, probably pekingese, were trained to stand still with candles held in their mouths. Coming to more recent times again, the use of truffle hounds was once quite common in England, but even these have vanished from the scene.

The truffle is an underground fungus that has for centuries been valued as a food and seasoning. The high price, as much as 10 or even 15 shillings a pound, that it fetched in the nineteenth century made the search for it very worth while, and a number of people even made this a full-time occupation. The dog was a valued assistant in this work, for his sense of smell was needed to locate the fungus.

Other animals also possess keen noses, of course, and some truffle hunters thought more highly of pigs than of dogs. These were commonly used in the Perigord region of France, but only a small minority of the English trufflers favored them. One of this minority was a man named William Leach, who, having come over from the West Indies with a team of trained hogs, spent four years surveying southern England before finally settling on Patching, in Sussex, as the best spot to ply his trade.

Truffle hunting is not the only sphere in which pigs have been set up in rivalry to dogs. Unlikely as it sounds, they have even been employed in hunting. In the Middle Ages, the forest laws forbade commoners to keep dogs considered large enough for hunting unless they had been "expedited," an operation that entailed cutting off toes from the forefeet so that the animal would be unable to run down the game. It was to evade this regulation that the more determined and ingenious poachers began to use pigs instead of dogs, and apparently found them efficient substitutes. The only hunting pig of which much is known is one called Slut, which belonged to Sir Henry Mildmay. According to *Rural Sports* (1807), it started its sporting career at the age of eighteen months and was regarded as excelling the best of pointers.

Other hunting animals of which considerable use has been made include ferrets and various members of the cat family. The big cat chiefly associated with hunting is the cheetah, which is still tamed for this purpose. The ancient Egyptians liked to hunt with it and, according to Marco Polo, Kublai Khan maintained large numbers of the beasts. This monarch did everything on the grand scale. He numbered his hunting dogs in thousands and even appears to have made use of semitamed tigers. He was excessively fond of falconry, and his household included ten thousand falconers to look after the birds. Falconry, or hawking, was also very popular in medieval Europe, and it was elaborated into a ritual in which each rank of chivalry was allotted an appropriate bird to use.

As well as this type of hunting, one or two birds have also been trained to fish. Of these the cormorant is by far the best known. Its use is generally associated with China, but the idea of training it appears to have originated in Japan. A ring is fastened around the bird's neck, tight enough to prevent it swallowing any but the smallest fish, and a harness is put about its body so that its movements can be controlled by the fisherman. It is so adept at its work that a single bird will some-times catch as many as a hundred fish in an hour.

Incidentally, the only fish to be taken into man's service, the remora, also serves the fishermen. This fish is a peculiar creature that makes use of the suction disc on its head to attach itself to larger fish or any other moving object and so get free transport from place to place. When a captive remora is lowered into the water by a fisherman, the idea is that it should fasten itself to a turtle which it will continue to cling to as it is pulled up to the surface.

Fishing, like the employment of ibis as cattle guards in parts of Africa and of unfortunate geese as involuntary chimney sweeps in nineteenth century rural Ireland, must be accounted among the minor uses that have been made of birds. Of much greater importance is the use of the pigeon to carry messages. It is not the only bird to have been ex-ploited in this way but it has proved to be by far the most valuable. Man-of-war birds were sometimes used in the Pacific area, especially by the early missionaries, but they did not have the reliability of the homing pigeon, which has been valued ever since the days of the ancient Egyptians.

The Romans made use of pigeons to carry messages, and the practice remained common in the Near East. Egypt especially, had a well-organized pigeon post during the rule of the Mamelukes, from the thirteenth to the sixteenth centuries. The Crusaders learned the use of the carrier pigeon from the Saracen armies and introduced it to western Europe. The value of the pigeon post was demonstrated during the siege of Paris in the Franco-Prussian War, 1870–71, when some four hundred pigeons kept the citizens in touch with the outside world and carried between them over a million communications. This striking achievement inspired

Homing pigeons have been reliable messengers since ancient times; their services were even recognized officially during World War II.

the news agencies, especially the famous Reuters, to organize their own pigeon post systems.

The birds retained their military value even during the Second World War, and the work they did received official recognition when, in 1946, a U.S. Army pigeon named G.I. Joe was flown across the Atlantic to be invested with the Dickin Medal, the animals' Victoria Cross, at a special ceremony in the Tower of London.

Even if they are no longer needed to maintain communications, pigeons may still have a part to play in military affairs. By means of modern, scientifically devised methods of training they could easily be taught to guide bombs or other missiles to their targets. The feasibility of this guidance system was actually known and demonstrated during the Second World War, but it was not used—not because of moral scruples but more probably because such reliance on an animal associate was regarded as a backward step in a mechanized age.

The orthodox military mind has perhaps always been suspicious of such ideas. Even in ancient times, when the use of animals in war was so much more general, only a few commanders had enough imagination to use their animal allies to the fullest advantage. One of these few, and possibly the most ingenious of them, was the Carthaginian leader Hannibal. On one occasion he even made effective use of poisonous snakes. This happened toward the end of his career, after the defeat of Carthage, when he was fighting for the king of Bithynia against Pergamum. He advised the king to have the serpents collected, put into earthenware jars and catapulted into the ships of the enemy. This was done, and although the sailors of Pergamum at first laughed heartily at the sight of the Bithynians preparing to throw pots at them, they lost their grins when the pots broke and hundreds of snakes crawled and slithered over their ship. They soon decided they had had enough and surrendered.

Above all else, though, Hannibal is especially associated with elephants because of his famous march over the Alps. This really constitutes one of the ironies of history since, despite all the difficulties overcome in that epic, only one of the elephants survived long enough to play much part in his Italian campaign. Even if they had all lived, the effort might still not have been worth while, for by Hannibal's day the Romans had long since grown out of the terror inspired by their first encounters with the huge creatures.

Elephants had a frightening effect on all armies when they met them for the first time. Alexander the Great's Macedonians were the first Europeans to fight against them and, although they won their battles, the fear of the great beasts remained. It was this fear that was later partly responsible for the mutiny that halted Alexander's march into India and so altered the history of the world. Alexander himself had been impressed by the tactical advantages offered by these living engines of war and was anxious to press on to the lands where, as he had been informed, they abounded. His soldiers, however, dreaded further encounters with them and, disheartened by the hardships of living and marching through the monsoon rains, refused to continue eastward. They wanted to go home.

They took the news of the elephant back with them, and the animal itself was soon afterward introduced into the armies of some of the Mediterranean powers. It used to be thought that elephants were all obtained from India, but it is now known that the Egyptians, who were among the earliest of the non-Indian users of these animals, obtained them from Africa. In 280 B.C. they founded the settlement of Ptolemaïs Theron, on the Red Sea coast, as the center of their elephant-catching expeditions, and great numbers of the beasts were shipped from there to Egypt.

The Carthaginians also knew how to train the African elephant, a feat which would have surprised the ancient Indians who were long confident that they enjoyed an absolute monopoly of war elephants. This naturally gave them a feeling of superiority when they faced the armies of less fortunate nations. In an astute attempt to destroy this assurance and so gain a psychological advantage for herself, the Assyrian queen Semiramis (859–833 B.C.) is alleged to have put a number of fake elephants at the head of her army when she fought the Indian ruler Stabrobates.

The frauds were made up of the skins of black oxen stretched over light frames and carried by camels. The Indian king was undismayed by the sight of these monsters, for he had received prior information of the Assyrian plan, and he immediately led a cavalry charge against them. This boldness nearly lost him the battle, for his horses became difficult to

control when they came close enough to catch the scent. Semiramis promptly took advantage of the confusion to launch a counterattack, but Stabrobates retrieved the situation by sending his own elephants forward against the disguised camels, whereupon many of the latter were gored or trampled to death and the Assyrian host was defeated.

Indian faith in the invincibility of elephants remained almost unbroken until the wily invader Timor won a decisive victory against them in A.D. 1399. For his defensive measures against their attack he had a ditch dug around his encampment and ramparts built on which he strung the corpses of numerous

War elephants caused terror among their enemies until Roman commanders devised counter strategies.

buffaloes. The carcasses were surrounded by bramble and brushwood and were set on fire when the elephants charged. When he abandoned defense and led a cavalry charge against Sultan Mahmud's troops, he ordered his men to aim their sword blows against the trunks of the elephants. The great beasts were covered by iron plates bristling with spikes, swung heavy iron clubs to protect their heads and bodies and even, or so it is alleged, had poisoned daggers fastened to their trunks, but despite their armament they were unable to withstand this sort of attack and fled ignominiously, trampling on some of their own army in the process.

The idea of so harassing the elephants that they stampeded back into their own lines had occurred to the Roman commanders fairly soon after they first encountered them. When the elephants were orginally used against them, in 280 B.C. at the Battle of Heraclea, the legionaries fled, unable to withstand the force of the charge, and twenty-five years later, when they were fighting the Carthaginians, the elephants again easily broke through their lines. Even when the Romans strengthened their center, it was of no avail. The increased numbers merely meant that more were trampled to death. However, soon after this it became customary to dig a large trench to halt the charge of the animals and then to assail them with showers of arrows and spears so as to drive them back in confusion.

A little later Scipio countered an elephant charge even more simply by drilling his legionaries in a maneuver which opened their ranks and left wide avenues down which the animals ran more or less harmlessly. These successes removed all the terror inspired by the new weapon. The Roman soldiers gave the elephants the derisive name of "Lucanian cows," and the Carthaginian generals began to have serious doubts regarding their military effectiveness. Elephants were subsequently taken into the Roman army and even scored a few successes, one apparently having quite an effect on the natives of Britain. Nevertheless, they were never so important with the Romans as they had been with the Carthaginians. Generally speaking, the Romans preferred their elephants in the circus ring rather than the army.

CHAPTER 5

ANIMAL ENTERTAINMENTS

THE FIRST recorded appearance of elephants in the arena was in 251 B.C., when 142 of them—captured from the Carthaginians by L. Metellus—were exhibited as curiosities before being killed. The slaughter was organized not so much as a spectacle but as a means of removing an embarrassment, for apparently no one could think of what else to do with them. It was psychologically a valuable maneuver, though, for it demonstrated to the Romans that the monsters could be killed and that there was no reason for a superstitious fear of them.

However, mere butchery was not enough to satisfy Roman audiences for long. They liked to see plenty of blood, but they also demanded an atmosphere of chance and competition, something they could bet on. Consequently, chariot racing long remained their favorite entertainment. This was as well organized as present-day horse racing and much more exciting. The form of the horses and men was discussed and race cards were studied before the bets were placed. A race usually entailed seven dangerous laps of the circus, a distance of approximately six miles. The charioteers stood in the light two-wheeled chariots with the reins passing round their bodies so that they could use all their weight when necessary to check the horses. Because of this they also had to carry knives so as to cut themselves free if there was a crash.

Spills were frequent, but some of the charioteers were sufficiently skillful, or lucky, to enjoy long and successful careers. Some of them even made fortunes, for the winner of a race received a money prize in addition to a retaining fee from the stable he was representing. There were also gifts from grateful bettors. One of the most famous of the charioteers was Diocles, active in the second century A.D., who claimed to have won over four thousand races. He retired at the age of forty-two with a fortune estimated to be the equivalent of over $700,000 in modern currency.

Chariot racing remained immensely popular throughout Roman history, but it did eventually become a little outdone in spectacular appeal by the fights to the death of the gladiators and the animals. The first contest between animals was put on by M. Fulvius in 186 B.C. to celebrate the conquest of Syria, and proved to be so much to the Roman taste that similar spectacles soon became a regular feature of the shows.

Succeeding promoters tried hard to surpass each other's efforts and scoured the known world for strange beasts and spectacles to titillate the appetites of the crowd. Fighting elephants first appeared about the year 99 B.C. and were soon being matched against a variety of opponents, including bulls and dogs. In 58 B.C. Scaurus introduced crocodiles and a hippopotamus, and thirteen years later the giraffe made its first appearance at a series of games organized by Julius Caesar. Other rulers thrilled the crowds with the sheer numbers of the animals they exhibited and killed. In 55 B.C. Pompey put 18 elephants and a total of 600 lions into the arena, and as many as 9,000 animals are said to have been killed in the games with which the Emperor Trajan opened the Colosseum in A.D. 80.

The delight the Romans took in this sort of entertainment is sometimes regarded as a proof that they were a particularly cruel and insensitive race. This is not really fair, for the enjoyment of animal fights is something that seems to have been common to all races.

In Asia animal fights were organized from very ancient times. Indeed, it was from Asia that the idea was imported to Rome, and it is even possible that some of the earlier animals to appear in the Roman arenas came from oriental menageries rather than straight from the wild. Not only did the Asiatic contests predate the better-known Roman ones, but they continued to take place for centuries after the last animal had died in the Colosseum.

Elephant fights were especially popular in the East, and were as bloodthirsty as anything staged by the Romans. The riders of these fighting elephants were so frequently thrown down and killed that it became customary to have a reserve driver mounted in readiness behind the first man. Indeed, according to some Western travelers who later witnessed such fights, they were considered so dangerous that before a contest the drivers invariably took their farewells of their families. Even mere attendance was risky, as sometimes the pain-maddened elephants charged into the crowd and people were trampled on or crushed, either by the animals or by their panic-stricken fellow spectators.

None of this danger attended the equally popular battle between tigers and water buffalo, contests which excited a vengeful cruelty in the onlookers and which were far removed from any concept of sport. It was common practice to starve the tiger for some time after its capture so that it would be weakened by the day of the contest, and it was also cruelly goaded and teased. A nineteenth century writer describing one such fight said that the tiger was so weakened and so reluctant to fight that it had to be forced out of its cage with blazing bundles of bamboo. Even when it did come out, its only idea was to escape, and it attempted to climb the fence that surrounded the enclosure. This effort was foiled by a barrage of stones and the vigorous wielding of pikes and further blazing torches. The unfortunate tiger tumbled down the fence, straight on to the horns of the waiting buffalo. It was tossed high into the air and lay where it fell. The spectators were not to be cheated of their sport, however, and scalding water and more fire eventually roused the tiger to another escape attempt. This was repulsed in the same way as before and again the animal fell onto the buffalo's horns and was this time finally gored and trampled to death.

Although they aroused great enthusiasm, these contests could never be more than occasional delights, dependent as they were upon the successful trapping of a tiger. Consequently they were never able to rival the immense appeal of cock-fighting, which probably originated in the Far East and has been a favorite sport there for thousands of years. Even today it is still followed with passionate interest, especially in Malaya and Indonesia. Almost everyone owns a cock, and there is frenzied gambling on the fights.

Practically all nations have at some time or other succumbed to the savage lure of cock-fighting, though it has nowhere else become the cult that it is in the East. Nevertheless it does have a strong appeal for many, and so continues to some extent even in countries like the United States where it has been banned by law. In 1966 newspapers carried stories of a successful police raid on one such illegal cockfight in the woods at Saginaw, Michigan: sixty-six spectators were startled when a police plane swooped low overhead and a loud speaker blared that they were under arrest. Escape through the woods was impossible because state policemen in camouflage uniforms came out from behind the trees. The only problem left to the police was what to do with the hundred or more birds they had confiscated.

In Britain, too, cock-fighting has long been outlawed, but occasional reports show that it still has its devotees and is carried on surreptitiously. All this is a further reminder that a love of cruel sports is far from being the vice of any particular race or age. Indeed, Britain has a history of animal baiting and slaughter that matches that of ancient Rome in practically everything except the spectacular nature of the animals involved and the risk to human contestants.

Cruel as cock-fighting is, the pastime of cock-throwing is even worse, and it was for a long time widely practiced in Britain. It was a revolting business in which a cock was tied to a post and the contestants tried to kill it by throwing sticks. Of all the unlikely people, the renowned and saintly Sir Thomas More was devoted to this sport in his younger days and was considered to be an expert.

In the sixteenth century very few people saw anything to criticize in such conduct. Then and for a long time afterward any animal fight was sure of an appreciative audience. Innumerable contests were arranged between cats and dogs and between dogs and monkeys, and the enthusiasm of the crowds rose with the degree of ferocity shown by the contestants. Because the animals concerned were bigger and

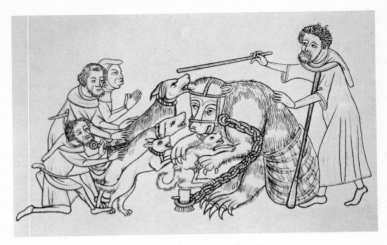

The popular entertainment of bearbaiting was not stamped out until the nineteenth century.

presumably more savage, the baiting of bulls and bears was especially popular.

Bearbaiting depended very largely on the support of the rich, since bears were expensive animals, and it gradually died out as first theater-going and then horse racing and fox hunting became more fashionable pursuits. Bulls were obtained more easily, however, and the baiting of them long remained a favorite entertainment of the mob. It was not completely stamped out until well into the nineteenth century, and relics of it, such as the stones or iron rings to which animals were tethered, remain in many places up and down the country. There is a living memorial, too, in the shape of the bulldog, a type of dog that was especially bred for this sport.

The 1835 act that forbade bullbaiting and similar sports was not passed without a desperate struggle, and its most obstinate opponents were the townsfolk of Stamford, in Lincolnshire, where a bull run had been traditional since the reign of King John (1204–15).

Every November a half-crazed bull was pursued through the streets by a pack of barking, snapping dogs and a mob of shouting, screaming citizens, in a nightmare of senseless noise and violence. Spectators lined the streets in a series of wagons and carts and shouted their approval and appreciation as the bull was hacked and beaten to death. The people of Stamford so clung to this traditional sport that they ignored the new law and bitterly resented any attempts to enforce it. When the secretary of the Royal Society for the Prevention of Cruelty to Animals visited a sympathizer in Stamford to discuss what action should be taken, he was warned that if it became known he was in town, he would be in grave danger of mob violence.

The bull run took place again in 1836, and the society succeeded in getting three people convicted at the Lincoln Assizes, but nevertheless the event was held yet again in 1837. The Stamford magistrates sought to justify this by quoting the ancient charter, but the Lord Chief Justice ruled that bull running was illegal. The government was so annoyed at the flouting of its authority that in 1838 twelve policemen, supported by a company of dragoons, were sent up from London to enforce the law and it was made plain that any rioters would be dealt with very firmly.

Bulls have always suffered severely in the name of sport. Some prehistoric cave paintings are thought to depict a form of bullfighting, and bulls played a vital part in the games of ancient Crete. These games were probably religious in character and demanded amazing acrobatic ability from the performers, who were expected to somersault over the back of a charging animal. Apart from the incredible agility of these performers, the most remarkable thing concerning these games is that the bulls were apparently not killed. In almost every other age and culture the sport has been judged by the amount of blood shed.

Many thousands of animals have been butchered in the bullfights which are still so popular in Spain and various other countries. Here the bull has no hope. The whole purpose of the entertainment is to achieve a kill, and no matter how well or bravely the bull fights, its doom is certain from the moment it enters the ring. When the Spanish set up colonies in America, the bullfight was one of the things they took with them, which is why it is as well established today in Mexico as it is in Spain itself. California was also a Spanish colony, but there, as well as enjoying the traditional sport, the settlers introduced a variation of their own, in which fighting bulls were matched against the native grizzly bears.

These contests were as unsavory as any of the animal-baiting sports, but before any contests could take place, the bears had to be caught, and the bravery shown at this stage of the proceedings almost excused the subsequent cruelty. The catching was done by four horsemen using lassos, and in the days before a proper technique was developed it must have been foolhardily dangerous. Not only is a thousand-pound grizzly a formidable opponent at the best of times, but there was the added difficulty of controlling the horses, which were commonly flung into a panic by the scent of the bears. To catch one in this way it was necessary to get so close, it was a wonder that even the best trained of horses could be controlled.

The idea of the would-be captors was to get their ropes round the the limbs of the bear and then pull in different directions so that its enormous strength could be contained by their combined efforts. The frightening noise and confusion as the men shouted and the horses pulled and reared

*In Minoan Crete the stylized sport of bull
leaping required graceful, agile performers.*

as they tried to check the rushes of the enraged and snarling
grizzly can be easily imagined. It is not at all surprising that
the animal often won the contest, sometimes killing a man
or a horse in the process.

Nor was this the whole of the battle. The riskiest part came
when the bear was successfully held by the four ropes. It then
had to be pulled on to its back while one of the men ap-
proached it on foot and tied another lasso around its forepaws
and neck. However exhausted the animal appeared to be,
this always set off another flurry of activity which did not
end until it was securely fastened in what was almost a cocoon
of ropes. It was then transported to the town where the great
contest between bear and bull was due to take place.

These grizzlies were not starved or otherwise ill-treated like the tigers that fought in Java, but in order to make sure that two animals would fight each other, they were sometimes fastened together by a rope around their front legs. The bears usually won the fights, some of them dispatching as many as six bulls in succession, but they often had to take a lot of punishment and the bulls were victorious sufficiently often to make it worth while betting on the results. The contests remained popular in the West even after the Spanish era, for they provided just the sort of amusement that the rough-and-ready miners and cowboys of the 1850s appreciated, and the appearance of a bear with a good fighting reputation was sure to draw a large crowd.

Bulls still provide sport in North America, for they feature in some of the most exciting events of the popular rodeo. One of the really tough parts of these contests comes when the cowboys have to try to stay on the back of a bull for eight seconds. That does not sound very long, but the bulls are harder to ride than the wildest horses, and quite frequently it happens that no contestant manages to last the required time. When one comes off he has to run to safety before the bull can gore or trample him.

Another of the rodeo events, the bull-dogging, is almost exactly the same as a spectacle that used to thrill the crowds at the Roman Colosseum. In this, a cowboy has to fling himself from his horse, seize the horns of a steer and attempt to force it to the ground. The Roman equivalent was introduced into the arena by Julius Caesar when he imported Thessalonian horsemen to chase bulls and wrestle them to the ground by gripping their horns and twisting their necks.

The ways in which many other animals are used in entertainments such as films and circuses are also often almost identical in form and spirit to the Colosseum spectacles. Many

animal scenes in films have been designed to satisfy the demand for blood and savagery, and a number of circus and
music-hall acts cater to what is possibly an even more ignoble
fondness for ridicule. The Romans were not content with
teaching their performing elephants remarkable feats of
balance and other acts, but had to dress them up in tawdry
finery and costumes to get laughs as well, and this lamentable
custom still has many imitations today.

Of course the film maker has many advantages when it
comes to putting over animal effects, and by the judicious use
of the tricks of his trade he is often able to produce startling
results. The use of animals on the stage is much more difficult
and restricted. Nevertheless, ingenious producers have sometimes found it worth while to tackle the problems and have
contrived some astonishingly effective and exciting scenes
involving many different species of animals.

Toward the end of the nineteenth century Drury Lane
Theatre was particularly famous for its use of animals. Tremendous horse-racing scenes were arranged, with real horses
at full gallop and there was even a full-scale representation
of the chariot-racing scene from *Ben Hur,* with three chariots,
each drawn by four horses, careering around the stage. Like
the horse racing, this was managed by having each contestant
stationed on a separate moving strip of stage. This ensured
that the hero always won, as the final positions depended not
on the relative speeds of the horses but on the rate at which
the different platforms were made to revolve.

Such elaborate scenes are no longer presented today, but
the horse still plays an important part in sport and entertainment. Horse racing has changed from a sport to an industry
and, due very largely to television, is now watched and enjoyed by millions. Television is also responsible for the

*The modern circus was invented in 1769, when
a trick rider roped off a ring for his performance.*

tremendous upsurge of public interest in show-jumping, which
would otherwise remain the interest of a very small minority.

More than anything else, though, the horse is the embodi-
ment of the circus. This is as it should be, for not only is
it still the most important of the circus animals, but it was
directly responsible for the invention of that form of entertainment as it is known today. This happened in 1769, when
former Sergeant-Major Philip Astley, a trick rider, roped off
a ring because he found it easier to stand on his horse's back
if it was cantering in a circle. He was also the first to supplement his own trick riding performance with tumblers, slack
rope balancers and even a clown, and so ensured for himself permanent fame as the founder of the circus.

His shows became steadily bigger and more spectacular,
and his successor, Andrew Ducrow, added troupes of wild
beasts to the horse acts and so made the performances super-

ficially even more like those of the present day. There was a vast difference, though, in the way the animal acts were presented.

It was taken for granted that the only way to make wild beasts such as lions and other big cats perform was to dominate them through fear, and so they received the most vicious treatment. Whips, blank cartridges and goads were freely used and a lot of training was done with red-hot pokers. The animal was forced into making the required moves and actions by being burned with one of these, so that in the actual show it could be coerced by the sight of the stick with a blob of red sealing wax stuck on the end.

The shows themselves were often as barbaric as the methods of training. Everything possible was done to arouse the excitement of the audiences; performances were a crescendo of noise, and it was the job of the trainer to make his charges appear to be savage and dangerous. This was easily done since the conditions were calculated to stretch the animals' nerves to breaking point. Consequently, as the acts were usually performed in a cage measuring only about sixteen feet by ten feet, gruesome accidents were almost a commonplace of nineteenth century circus life.

This all helped to draw the crowds. Indeed, the public appetite for horrors was such that the frequent genuine accidents were not enough to satisfy it and so fakes had to be arranged. The use of fire and smoke in the animal acts helped these deceptions. When the audience's view was obscured, the trainer would start to shriek and to shout for help, and would then stagger into sight dripping with blood, which had been thrown over him by an assistant as he came out of the cage.

The circus began to reform itself about the end of the

nineteenth century, thanks very largely to Carl Hagenbeck, the son of a Hamburg fish-shop keeper and animal dealer. He and his brother Wilhelm became the world's foremost animal dealers, ran the celebrated Hagenbeck circus, and in 1897 opened the Stellingen Tierpark, the world's first zoo without bars.

Hagenbeck was certain that the best results would be achieved by kindness and an understanding of animal psychology, and in 1880 set out to prove this revolutionary theory. Other showmen were impressed when his trainer, Dayerling, perfected an act in which three lions were harnessed to a two-wheeled chariot and driven round the ring. Convinced by this "impossible" feat of the merits of his system, they too began to study and apply Hagenbeck's theories of gentling. Nowadays, very few animal trainers still rely on the old methods of severity.

The changeover was accelerated by the growing demand for a new type of animal act. During the nineteenth century the public had been made increasingly aware of the need for a change in the general attitude toward animals. At the beginning of the century thinking men had become revolted by the widespread cruelty and the general indifference to animal suffering, and their indignation gradually spread.

Many people still refuse to accept that animals can be trained without cruelty and campaign vigorously to have all animal acts barred by law. In the United States even the traditional sport of the rodeo has been under fire from humane societies. Most of the complaints have been about such devices as flank straps and the use of electric shocks on the animals, but Friends of Animals, Inc., launched a national campaign to have rodeos banned entirely. This was so successful that some states have recently seriously considered outlawing the sport, thus going far beyond the actions taken by others such as New York, Ohio and West Virginia in passing restrictive legislation. The general public, however, seems to have remained unimpressed by the propaganda, for the International Rodeo Association reported that over 12,000,000 people attended the 1,500 shows held in 1966.

CHAPTER 6

ZOOS AND MENAGERIES

*

THE PEOPLE WHO condemn the use of performing animals in circuses and rodeos often extend their criticisms to zoos, arguing that the deprivation of liberty is cruel and that prisoners lead unnatural lives. This viewpoint is often presented in a simple and dramatic way by the question, "How would you like to be shut up in a cage?" It then sounds both reasonable and unanswerable. To zoologists, however, such a question is meaningless. They are too well aware that the implication, that animals share the attitudes of human beings and understand such concepts as freedom and captivity, is entirely false.

The consciousness of wild animals is concerned almost solely with the problem of remaining alive and of satisfying physical needs and instincts.

Consequently, when all its needs are met the animal is content, and that contentment is not the least bit impaired by the bars of a cage. Indeed, zoo keepers find that one of their problems arises because animals frequently become too content. In their wild state they would move no farther than they needed to satisfy their wants, and since in a zoo everything is provided on the spot they see no need to move at all. Some zoos that have put their animals in large enclosures have found they make little use of the new space and freedom of movement. Sometimes even people who have no moral objections to keeping animals in cages become indignant and charge those who run the zoos with neglect of the exhibits. They complain because they find the smell of some of the dens objectionable and, because they do not understand the psychology of the animals, think it indicates slackness on the part of the authorities. Animals, however, are not bothered by human notions of hygiene and aesthetics. The great majority of male animals regularly mark out their own territories, either by urination or by gland secretions, and would feel most lost and unhappy in sterile, scent-free surroundings. To them it is the smell that makes the cage or den recognizable as home.

This does not mean that no criticisms of zoos are ever justified. That is unfortunately far from being the case. Zoos vary tremendously in their standards, and there is no doubt at all that in some, conditions leave much to be desired. Sometimes the living quarters are unsuitable, and occasionally the animals appear to be regarded only as exhibits to be shown off and so their welfare comes a poor second to the entertainment of the pubilc.

Such zoos are, however, few and far between, and in most of them everything possible is done to ensure the animals' welfare. Even if more humane considerations were not also involved, this would merely be sound common sense since the stock of a zoo represents a considerable, and in many cases an extremely large, capital investment. The majority of zoos are never complacent about their facilities and conditions, but are continually striving to improve them. This can be expensive. Recently, for example, the London Zoo spent £120,000 (about $336,000) on a new aviary, and a year's expenditure at the San Diego Zoo ran to about $3,250,000.

Generally speaking, the only cruelty that the animals are likely to meet with comes from the visitors to the zoos. This is sometimes deliberate, and some Continental zoos have reported shocking cases of attacks on the animals, but is more often the unintentional result of ignorance. The worst offenders are those who insist on feeding the animals even when they are clearly and plainly requested not to do so. This can be bad enough when it only causes overfeeding, but all too often the proffered fare is wildly unsuitable. Because the animals know no better than to accept such things, a certain type of person finds it irresistibly funny to offer them the most bizarre tidbits, even including knives and pieces of broken glass. In 1923 the first rhinoceros to reach the Edinburg Zoo died a few months after arrival, its stomach badly torn by one such gift, and in the same zoo thirty years later another rhinoceros died from a similar cause. Most zoos can report similar tragedies.

The idea of zoos probably originated in China, where Emperor Wen, who ruled in the twelfth century B.C., kept a large collection of animals from the various provinces over which he ruled. This habit spread, and an inscription dating from about 950 B.C. tells how Ashurcasirpal II of Syria captured lions, ostriches, elephants and many other animals and brought them to his city of Kalakh to "let the people of my lands see them all."

The Egyptians maintained large temple menageries, and the Empress Hatshepsut organized the first animal-collecting expedition when she sent a special fleet to Punt to bring back species of dogs, monkeys, leopards and giraffes. In classical

Rhinoceroses and other zoo animals often fall victim to such tidbits as knives and broken glass.

times the soldiers of Alexander the Great brought back strange creatures for the scientists to study and the populace to gape at, and the famous war elephants of Carthage were put on show in a public park when they were not needed for military use. There were also well-stocked menageries in Rome, though these were usually devoted to supplying the arena. In 29 B.C. the collection of Octavius Augustus was reported to contain 260 lions, 420 tigers and a further 600 assorted African animals, among them a rhinoceros, a hippopotamus and an enormous serpent 82 feet long.

Until the rebirth of zoo keeping in the nineteenth century, the only menageries to rival this in size were those of Kublai Khan in the thirteenth century and of the Aztec Emperor Montezuma three hundred years later. According to Marco

Polo, Kublai Khan's magnificent collection even included the hippopotamus and, in addition to the main menagerie of such animals as lions, tigers and leopards, a separate extensive stable of elephants and rhinoceroses. Montezuma's zoo was less dramatic since America does not possess the same variety of large, exotic mammals. It contained such animals as were available, however, and also housed large numbers of snakes as well as what was described as an almost complete collection of the birds of the continent.

There was never anything like these two collections in Europe despite the revival of court menageries during the later Middle Ages. The Renaissance princes vied with each other in obtaining rarities and were prepared to pay enormous prices for particularly exotic specimens, but none built up a really extensive permanent collection. Nor did they seem to bother very much about breeding the animals, preferring to replenish their numbers when necessary by purchase or by soliciting gifts from friendly rulers in Egypt and the East. The finest of the European menageries was the papal zoo, founded in the sixteenth century by Pope Leo X. Naturally all the princes of Christendom were pleased to contribute, and it soon contained quite a varied collection.

One of the highlights of its history was the arrival in 1514 of an elephant, the gift of the king of Portugal. Elephants were most unusual sights in sixteenth century Europe, and this present was very gratefully accepted, even though the beast disgraced himself on arrival by squirting a trunkful of water over the Pope and assembled dignitaries.

Between the fall of Rome and the sixteenth century only two elephants had been seen in Europe. One of these had been presented to Charlemagne by the caliph of Baghdad in 797 and the other was a gift to Henry III from Louis IX of France in 1254.

Henry III was the first English monarch to become enthusiastic about collecting strange animals, and in order to house the gifts he solicited from foreign kings, he enclosed a large park at Woodstock, Oxfordshire. Following the receipt of three leopards from the Emperor Frederick II, however, all the royal animals were removed to quarters in the Tower of London. The menageries thereupon remained a feature of the Tower until 1834, when the collection was transferred to the London Zoo.

It is doubtful if the citizens of thirteenth century London appreciated the menagerie at first, for they had to pay for its upkeep. In 1252 the sheriffs were ordered to find fourpence a day for the keep of a white bear. They also had to provide the muzzle and chain used when the animal was allowed to swim in the Thames for exercise, or to catch fish. Three years later there was the expense of building a house forty feet long and twenty feet wide to accommodate the king's elephant.

The transport of this beast across the Channel must have been an epic feat in one of the cockleshell ships of the time, and a tremendous amount of interest was aroused. Even the dissatisfaction about the expense of the menagerie vanished temporarily in the excitement, and going to the Tower to gape at the monster became so much the thing to do that this could almost be said to mark the beginning of the menagerie as a popular entertainment in England.

Another royal elephant arrived in 1623, sent, along with five camels, as a gift from the king of Spain to James I, who was fascinated by animals and kept a private menagerie in

St. James's Park. The monarch was so delighted by the present that he rewarded the keeper who delivered the animals with the princely gift of £150. The king was so proud and so jealous of his new possessions that special orders were given to prevent them from being disturbed or devalued by the rude gaze of the vulgar. The camels were grazed in the park but were returned to their stables under cover of night, and the elephant was not even taken out to be watered but was instead allowed a daily ration of a gallon of wine.

During the centuries the fortunes of the Tower menagerie fluctuated, and by the nineteenth century they were at a very low ebb. In 1822 its only inhabitants were an elephant, a grizzly bear and several birds. Fortunately, a more enthusiastic keeper then took over, and by 1829 the collection had regained something of its former splendor.

By the beginning of the nineteenth century the animals in the Tower were rivaled by another permanent London collection at Exeter Change, in the Strand, where Pidcock's menagerie was established. The front of this building was most gaudily painted with monsters and wild beasts, and there were barkers dressed as yeomen of the guard stationed outside to extol the wonders that were on view within and so persuade passers-by to part with a half-crown admission fee. The roaring of the beasts could be heard quite clearly from the roadway, frightening horses and sometimes causing traffic mishaps, to the delight of the publicity-conscious showman.

The most notable of the animals to be exhibited in Exeter Change was probably Chunie, an elephant who achieved a melancholy fame by the manner of his death in 1826. He was described by his exhibitor, Mr. Cross, one of Pidcock's successors, as an "animated mountain," and was advertised as the largest animal ever to be shown in Europe. Unfortunately he became afflicted with severe toothache, and this changed him from an amiable, good-humored creature to a raging monster.

His tantrums and noise threw the whole of Exeter Change into an uproar, and it soon became obvious that he would have to be destroyed before things got completely out of hand. A nearby gunmaker was applied to for rifles, but the volunteer marksmen failed to hit him in the vital spot, possibly through ignorance, or, perhaps, because they were unnerved by the tumult. Enraged all the more by his wounds, the elephant made frantic efforts to get at his tormentors, but was repelled by the ten-feet-long double-edged spears of the attendants. Another six shots were fired without very much effect and then a file of soldiers arrived from Somerset House. Even then round after round had to be poured into him before Chunie eventually succumbed. It must have been a nightmare scene, with the other birds and beasts frightened and noisy, but half hidden by the smoke that wreathed across the hall as the soldiers fired steadily into the great bulk of the screaming, struggling elephant.

The terrible ignorance demonstrated by this barbarous episode was shown also by the general treatment and caging of the animals in both Exeter Change and the Tower menagerie. Even unsentimental eighteenth century visitors to the Tower had thought "the poor beasts very badly housed," and at the Change the main concern of the proprietors was to crowd in as many animals as possible. The consequent stench and noise, especially when one of the larger exhibits was provoked into throwing itself against the bars in a vain effort to reach a tormentor, can easily be imagined.

There was an element of danger in teasing the animals into such displays, for the cages used in those days were often not particularly secure. The two permanent London collections seem somehow to have avoided trouble, but there were numerous contemporary accounts of escapes from the traveling menageries. Undoubtedly some of these stories were concocted by showmen as a lure for sensation-seeking customers, but many were genuine. Ballard's Menagerie benefited by a great deal of publicity, and extra business, when a lion escaped and made a sensational attack on the Exeter mail coach, springing on one of the horses and wounding it dreadfully. It subsequently killed a mastiff before being recaptured.

The first menagerie of which any details remain was Pidcock's, which took to the road in 1708. There were soon a number of them in existence, but the best known and the biggest was undoubtedly Wombwell's founded in 1805. George Wombwell had been a shoemaker, but he became a showman after acquiring a pair of boa constrictors, then a great novelty in England, from a sailor. He bought the snakes for £75, put them on show, and within three weeks had made a handsome profit. This decided him upon his new career, and he went on to become one of the foremost wild beast exhibitors in the country, with three large shows on the road.

In these days of a surfeit of entertainment it is hard to realize the degree of interest that was taken in these animal shows and in the Regent's Park Zoo when it opened in 1828. It is true that the newspapers were at first critical of this latter venture, dubbing it the work of the Noah's Ark Society, but this attitude soon changed and was forgotten, and the various newspapers and magazines competed with each other to give the most generous coverage to zoo topics and activities. The arrival of any especially noteworthy specimens provoked the sort of interest that is nowadays reserved for pop groups.

*Jumbo's sale to P. T. Barnum caused an outcry in England
and brought the American entrepreneur invaluable publicity.*

When four giraffes were brought over from Nubia in
1836, the excitement was so intense that a special appeal had
to be made to the public to remain quiet and orderly so as
not to disturb the exotic creatures. In addition, traffic was kept
off the route they took from the docks to Regent's Park and
they were given a police escort.

Another burst of enthusiasm was aroused in the same year
by the arrival at the zoo of the first chimpanzee, so that, as
Theodore Hook commented in *Blackwood's Magazine*:

> "The folks in town are nearly wild
> To go and see the monkey child."

Some years later there was the same sort of rush to see

the first hippopotamus to be exhibited in England. This particular craze provoked Thomas Macaulay to remark caustically, "I have seen the hippopotamus both asleep and awake, and I can assure you that, asleep or awake, he is the ugliest of the works of God." However, people were not content with his assurance. They wanted to see the new wonder for themselves, and the annual attendance rose from 168,895 in 1849 to 360,402 in 1850.

Another example of the public interest in the zoo and in the zoo favorites came in 1882, when it was reported that the Zoological Society had agreed to sell Jumbo, the elephant, to the American showman Phineas T. Barnum for $10,000. The society regarded this as an astute business move, for Jumbo's temper had become increasingly uncertain with age and the previous year the zoo superintendent, A. D. Bartlett, had reported that it might soon be necessary to have him destroyed. To the public, however, the idea of selling Jumbo, especially to an American, was an outrage. England went Jumbo crazy and the sale became an important public issue.

A defense fund was set up to save him from such a fate, and letters of protest were sent to the newspapers, to the Zoological Society and even to Barnum himself. The showman was, of course, delighted, for he was getting the sort of publicity that no money could buy. When the *Daily Telegraph* asked what he would accept for the return of Jumbo, he replied that £100,000 would be no inducement to cancel the purchase. Consequently, despite all the anger and the tears and the sentiment and even an unsuccessful attempt to seek an injunction against the sale, Jumbo left for America in March 1852.

Jumbo had been in the zoo for sixteen years before he was sold, and although this does not sound very remarkable, it was a considerably longer residence than could be claimed for most of the exhibits at that time. Every possible care and attention was lavished on the animals that came to the zoo, but the galling truth remained that the animals carted around the country in the cramped cages of the traveling menageries were healthier and had a greater life expectancy than the comparatively pampered inmates of Regent's Park.

The zoo animals were dying, more often than not, as a result of mistaken kindness and overprotection. This was because it was taken for granted that when animals from the tropics were brought to a northern country, they were unable to adapt themselves to the severer climate and needed to be shielded from its vagaries. Consequently, they were given indoor dens in which the temperature was maintained at a tropical level and from which fresh air was most rigorously excluded. In fact such conditions were far from ideal and greatly increased the animals' susceptibility to disease.

The first person to realize where the zoos were going wrong, for the situation was not peculiar to Regent's Park but was common to all zoos, was Carl Hagenbeck, the man who did so much to improve conditions for circus animals. His observations convinced him that it was a fallacy to suppose that cold weather was fatal to the animals, and from the 1870s onward he conducted a number of acclimatization experiments to justify his belief. When he opened his zoo at Stellingen, near Hamburg, in 1897, he made sure that all the animals had free access to the open air throughout the year. He also designed it as the world's first cageless zoo, showing the animals in natural surroundings, separated from the spectators by unjumpable ditches instead of bars.

Such a radical departure from the accepted way of things provoked a great deal of criticism, but the more farsighted of the zoo authorities recognized the value of what he was doing and accepted it as the direction in which they must move. In England the principal apostle of the importance of fresh air was Dr. Peter Chalmers Mitchell, who became secretary to the Zoological Society of London in 1903. He made a full investigation into all the deaths that had been recorded at the zoo between 1870 and 1902 and contrasted the ages at which the animals had died with what their life expectancy would have been in the wild. It became immediately obvious that something was wrong at Regent's Park. Fortunately the statistics also hinted at the cure, for it became apparent that the few animals that had enjoyed a normal or extended life span were those that had been allowed outdoors.

The necessary reorganization of the zoo was an expensive business. Slowly, however, the cages were redesigned to give the animals access to fresh air, or, where this was not practicable, to give them the benefit of an adequate ventilation system. The value of this was soon reflected in the improved health of the animals. All this was not only scientifically encouraging but was also a big help in bringing back the crowds.

This revived public interest has been maintained. Although no new arrival at the zoo could hope to arouse the degree of excitement of the first giraffe or hippopotamus, a well-publicized birth such as that of the polar bear cub Brumas in 1949 can be guaranteed to draw in enormous crowds. Even without such special attractions, the number of annual visitors to the London Zoo remains very high, and there are now over thirty other zoos and aquaria up and down the country also doing brisk business.

Scarcely a nation in the world today is without at least one collection of animals, and the total annual attendances at all the world's zoos is estimated at over 150,000,000. One recent set of figures lists 5,000,000 visitors a year for the Mexico City Zoo and over 4,000,000 for Barcelona. Six other zoos— Tokyo, Peking, Moscow, the Giza Zoological Gardens in Cairo, the Lincoln Park Zoo in Chicago and the National Zoological Park in Washington, D.C.—each claimed more than 3,000,000 visitors.

Of course the number of visitors and the size of the zoo are not the only criteria of quality. Indeed, most of the major zoos have long since discarded the old naïve belief that success is measured by the size of the collection. The Bronx Zoo in New York is one that has openly abandoned attempted comprehensiveness and competitive collecting as part of its policy. This was an important decision because undoubtedly the anxiety of zoos to possess rare specimens has been a serious threat to many animal populations in the past. Capturing wild animals is usually a very wasteful process, for all too often several die for every one captured alive. When baby gibbons are caught by shooting the mothers down from their perches high up in the trees, the babies often die as well, either from the shots or from the fall.

To avoid this sort of thing, and because all zoos are very conscious nowadays of the important role they have to play in animal conservation, ever greater efforts are being made to breed from zoo stock and thus avoid the further depletion of the wild populations. Even a few years ago this would have seemed an impossible dream with all but a few of the very common species, but a great deal more has been learned about animals recently and many successes recorded. American zoos have played a particularly notable part in this work. The first zoo breeding of chimpanzees was at the Bronx Zoo in 1920; a lowland gorilla was born in the Columbus, Ohio, zoo in December 1956, and was the first such baby to be successfully reared; in 1966 the Louisville, Kentucky, zoo reared the olingo for the first time, and the Oklahoma City Zoo achieved what was believed to be the first known birth of a pangolin in captivity.

Another recent and important success in the breeding of rare animals has been recorded by the San Diego Zoo, where there have been a number of hatchings of the giant Galápagos tortoises. These creatures, formerly a convenient source of fresh meat for buccaneers and whalers, had become so reduced in numbers by the twentieth century that it seemed possible, and even likely, that they would become extinct. In the 1920s an attempt was made to prevent this disaster. An expedition sponsored by the New York Zoological Society captured 180 young tortoises and settled colonies of them in various zoos in the United States, Bermuda, the Panama Canal Zone and Australia. Unfortunately, breeding results in these colonies were disappointing and very few of the eggs hatched.

To remedy this state of affairs, changes were made in the tortoise enclosure at San Diego and a large area of adobe soil was removed and replaced with river sand. The result was seen the following year, 1958, when 5 live tortoises were hatched from 12 eggs. The following years were disappointing, though, for no eggs were laid from 1958 to 1961. In the next four years over 200 eggs were laid but only 17 tortoises were hatched. Even so, this represented success, and tribute was paid to it at the conference of "The Role of Zoos in the International Conservation of Wild Animals," held at the San Diego Zoo in October 1966 to celebrate the fiftieth anniversary of its founding.

The fact that speakers at this conference came from as far afield as Tasmania, Thailand, Africa and England was a

The Phoenix Zoo's tenth baby oryx was born in January 1967.

reminder of the internationalism of modern zoos. This point was brought out by the editor of the *International Zoo Yearbook*. She told the conference that in 1966, 480 zoos returned the *Yearbook* questionnaires and so made information about their breeding successes and zoological research available to all.

The idea that zoos should be regarded as wild animal banks, places where populations of endangered species could be bred either for a subsequent return to the wild or for distribution to other zoos, has begun to be generally accepted. This means specialization, and one of the conclusions of a symposium on "Zoos and Conservation," held in London in 1964, was that each zoo should select one or two rare species that it was particularly well equipped to deal with and to concentrate on them. Acceptance of this idea meant that zoos would surrender their treasured single specimens of rare animals so that these could be brought together as breeding groups. To achieve this is one of the aims of the Wild Animal Propagation Trust in the United States.

The case of the Arabian oryx provides a very good example of what can be achieved by international cooperation in this way. When it seemed likely that the species would soon become extinct, the Fauna Preservation Society in London organized an expedition that captured three of the very few animals that survived in the wild. These were too few to form a breeding herd, but the London Zoo donated what proved to be the only female Arabian oryx to be found in any zoo in Europe or America, and the four animals, two pairs, were sent to the Arizona Zoological Society's Phoenix Zoo. There they were subsequently joined by five more beasts, one from the sheik of Kuwait's private zoo and two pairs presented by King Saud of Saudi Arabia. Thus by 1964 the nucleus of a breeding herd had been established. When Major Grimwood, who had led the Operation Oryx expedition, told the conference at San Diego about the venture he said that altogether "six governments, five zoos, a score of societies, clubs and major commercial organizations, and hundreds of private individuals in Arabia, Africa, Europe and America" had been directly involved.

Another example of international cooperation, unfortunately not so successful, came with the widely publicized attempt in 1966 to mate the London Zoo's giant panda, Chi-Chi, with the Moscow Zoo's An-An. Chi-Chi's Moscow honeymoon proved unproductive, but it is possible that further efforts will be made to mate the two animals. Meanwhile, the only zoo that has had any breeding success with giant pandas is in Peking, where the first giant panda ever to be bred in captivity was born in the autumn of 1963.

The giant pandas provide one of the fortunately rare examples of politics preventing the interchange of animals. London Zoo's Chi-Chi was originally intended for the United States, but while she was still in transit the authorities suddenly realized that she was from Red China and that her import would therefore be illegal. They refused to budge on this point, and so the panda went to London. She is probably the most valuable single animal in the zoo's collection.

A family group of giant pandas remains an unlikely exhibit for any Western zoo, but when other animals have been brought together in the appropriate numbers, invaluable information has been gained about their behavior and development. It is possible for zoos to record information that could be gathered in the wild only with extreme difficulty, if at all, and it is now becoming accepted that zoos are vitally important research centers for zoologists and even for sociologists, for it is by studying nature and the behavior of animals that man becomes better able to understand himself. This is a far cry from the days when a zoo was merely a place where one went to laugh or marvel at the animals. Zoo keepers themselves believe that zoos have three functions, each more important than the entertainment aspect; the first is educational, the second is to act as research centers to discover all available data about animals and the third is to become breeding centers for endangered species.

CHAPTER 7

SCIENTIFIC EXPLOITATION

*

UNTIL FAIRLY MODERN TIMES there was little enough done to relieve human suffering, so it is not surprising that animals were neglected. The idea of conducting expensive research merely in order to help animals, and wild animals at that, is very new. In fact it belongs almost exclusively to the twentieth century. The first animals to receive much veterinary attention was the horse because of its economic importance, but even so it usually had to suffer rough-and-ready treatment that could be as dangerous as the original disease. In the Middle Ages horse doctors were not even numerous enough to form a guild or to be regarded as members of a profession. Generally speaking, superstition ruled unchallenged, and even in the nineteenth century there were cases reported where one farm animal was burned alive as a scapegoat to save the remainder of a herd afflicted by disease. Once veterinary research did get under way, however, a tremendous amount of animal suffering began to be relieved.

One disease conquered as a result of veterinary research was anthrax, among the great historic scourges of sheep and cattle. The ancient Greeks gave this disease its name, which means coal, because of the way in which it burned up its victims, and this it continued to do unchecked for another two thousand years. It could not be beaten until its nature was fully understood, and even after the anthrax bacillus had been isolated and identified, agriculturists and scientists alike were slow to accept the theory that such a tiny organism could be the cause of the disease.

Eventually the great French scientist Louis Pasteur (1822–95) managed to produce an anthrax vaccine from these bacilli and announced that this had been successfully tested on sheep in the laboratory. There was widespread skepticism of this claim and eventually a public trial of its efficacy was arranged to take place in May 1881 at a farm near Melun. The countryside was then being ravaged by a virulent outbreak of anthrax, so there was feverish public interest in the experiment. On May 31st a large crowd gathered to watch Pasteur inject anthrax bacilli into a flock of sheep, half of which he had previously vaccinated. Then all France waited to see what would happen. Within a few days Pasteur's confident claims had been justified. The part of the flock that had been vaccinated was alive and well but the other animals were dead or dying from anthrax.

Since then many other animal diseases have been conquered, or at least brought under control, as a result of laboratory experiments on animals. Even so, the vastly greater proportion of such experiments have been concerned with human needs rather than those of other animals. It is no exaggeration at all to say that literally millions of animals have been sacrificed so that man's sufferings might be relieved. Most of these have died within the last century, for although man has been using animals for the cure of his illnesses and diseases for many thousands of years, it is only comparatively recently that there has been any question of careful experiments and research.

Many of the ancient remedies, so called, were out-and-out superstitions, relying often on various forms of sympathetic magic whereby the ailment was transferred to an animal. Thus our forefathers impaled live snails on thorns in order to cure themselves of warts and thought that one of the best treatments for epilepsy was to bury a black cock on the spot where the sufferer fell. In Cornwall an epidemic of measles presaged a bad time for cats, as the popular remedy was to cut off the left ear of one of these and then to swallow three drops of the blood in a glass of water. Minced mouse was a more general prescription for measles, and roast mice were devoured in large numbers to cure a variety of ailments ranging from bladder troubles to whooping cough.

All this sounds most unpleasant, but our ancestors were firmly convinced that to be effective, a medicine had to be nauseous. The sufferer from stomatitis, or thrush, had to submit to having a frog held in his mouth until it died, and swallowing live frogs was a recognized treatment for various internal troubles. The unfortunate creatures were believed to suck out the poisons that were causing the discomfort. A similar idea was demonstrated by the wearing of a live toad against any part of the body afflicted by cancer so that it might draw out the malignancy.

There was more justification for the use of leeches to suck blood and so relieve various conditions. They were being used long before the beginning of the Christian era, and though they have now vanished from orthodox medical practice, it is said that a leech remains an effective, though unpleasant-seeming, treatment for a black eye.

At one time these strange water creatures were so frequently applied and for such a variety of ailments that the doctors themselves became generally known as leeches. French doctors were especially enthusiastic in their use, so much so that by the nineteenth century they had exhausted their native supply and were importing them from all over Europe. As many as 27,000,000 a year were imported by France, and as each leech was expected to suck from an eighth of an ounce to a full ounce of blood at a single application, the annual loss of French blood must have been enormous. They were never used to quite the same extent in England but, even so, the annual imports ran into millions, and there are probably people still alive who remember them being used. Leeches were also used in America.

The use of leeches was understandable at a time when the medical profession believed in the theory of bloodletting, but it seems incredible that some of the other "remedies" and treatments survived for so long. Still, exceptional conditions could always be found to explain failures, and it was probably better to try anything, however unlikely to succeed, rather than merely submit to the course of the disease.

The man who, more than any other, believed in this testing of ideas by experiment, and thereby laid the foundations of modern medical science, was the English scientist William Harvey (1578–1657). His discovery of the circulation of the blood and the work of the heart was the result of innumerable experiments on "toads, serpents, frogs, house-snails, shrimps, crevisses and all manner of little fishes," as he put it. These martyrs to scientific progress were cut open while alive so that he could study the actions of their hearts and analyze the processes involved.

The increased interest in experimentation in the years that followed is demonstrated in the formation of a number of societies to investigate scientific matters and to disseminate the acquired information. In England, the Royal Society grew out of the meetings of a London club and was established in 1662 with a charter defining its object as "the improving of Natural Knowledge by experiment." Members contributed a shilling each a week to cover the cost of experiments that ranged from the valuable to the merely curious. Typical of the latter was the study of a spider's ability to escape from the center of a ring of unicorn horn.

In Italy the Medici family supported an Academy of Experiment that was maintained in Florence from 1657 to 1667, and in France Colbert founded the Académie des Sciences in 1666. Like the English society, this was under royal patronage, but whereas Charles II merely took a keen interest in what went on, the French king paid a pension to each of the twenty members of the Paris Académie and allowed them to hold their twice-weekly meetings in his library.

Animal experiments continued and increased in number and scope. In 1718 a Teddington clerygman, Stephen Hales, became the first man to measure blood pressure. Clergymen in those days were no more sentimental regarding animals than the rest of the population, and the Rev. Hales's straightforward way of going to work was to have a horse tied up and stretched on its back and then to insert a pipe into an artery and to measure the height to which the blood rose. A tremendous number of experiments were also performed by the great John Hunter (1728–93). He was fascinated by anything connected with the mechanisms of animals and added greatly to the store of biological knowledge. His fellow surgeons were aghast when on one occasion he proposed tying off an artery in a patient's leg, for they were sure that this would cause gangrene. Hunter, however, was able to proceed with confidence because he had previously performed a similar operation on a deer and had noted that the other blood vessels increased in size in order to maintain the flow of blood.

Despite all this, only a minority of these early experiments led to any direct advances in medical practice. Deliberate experiment to discover the causes of disease and to test possible cures and treatments was a much later development. Anatomical and physiological knowledge was advanced but, apart from this, the early experimenters were more interested in physics and chemistry. It was, therefore, more a case of animals being the objects of research. Nevertheless, they had vital parts to play in many important discoveries. To give but two examples, Joseph Priestley (1733–1804) made use of mice in his investigations into the nature of oxygen, and thanks to the experiments of Luigi Galvani (1737–98) frogs can be said to have helped to found the era of electricity.

The revolutionary idea of using diseased animals and animals that had been deliberately infected with disease in order to cure or prevent the same or allied diseases in men began in the West with the work of Edward Jenner (1749–1823), who discovered the principle of vaccination against smallpox. His work was stimulated by the belief of his country patients that dairymaids could not catch smallpox and by the statement made by one patient to the effect that she was immune to smallpox because she had previously had the milder disease of cowpox.

Nevertheless, medicine did not really benefit spectacularly from experiments on laboratory animals until toward the end of the nineteenth century. It was then inspired by Pasteur, who had managed to establish the germ theory of disease and so provoked the researchers into a flurry of activity. One of his most dramatic series of experiments, which increased his already world-wide reputation and turned him into a living legend, was that which he conducted in his fight against hydrophobia.

The average person nowadays has little idea of just how

Louis Pasteur's series of experiments on rabbits led to the development of an anti-rabies serum and the saving of many lives.

savage this disease is, nor of how widespread it was until comparatively recently. The nineteenth century textbooks described hydrophobia, or rabies, as possibly the most agonizing form of suffering known to man, and at that time it was claiming a great many victims every year. Death came after a progression of convulsions, during which involuntary spasms of the throat and larynx produced strange sounds, which inspired the belief that the victim would die barking like the mad dog that had bitten him. Anything to do with water or other liquids, even the sound or smell of them, was enough to bring on one of the attacks.

The shocking nature of hydrophobia made it so feared that in medieval times the unfortunate sufferers were treated with terror-inspired cruelty. Some were even burned alive and others were buried up to their necks in the ground so that they were securely imprisoned and could not approach the uninfected. The kill-or-cure method of tying the victim into a sack and throwing him into a river was also occasionally tried.

The advocated cures of succeeding centuries were less unfeeling but equally useless. Some people put their faith in charms, others favored sea bathing and others hopefully swallowed various revolting-sounding medicines. In 1866 a Buckinghamshire coroner was told that a five-year-old victim of hydrophobia had died after eating the liver of the mad dog that had bitten him, recovered from its body nine days after the animal had drowned.

Pasteur investigated all the old remedies and satisfied himself that they were valueless. He then conducted a long series of experiments during which he injected rabbits with saliva taken from mad dogs and also subjected them to actual bites from rabid animals. On one occasion, when a bulldog could not be provoked into biting the rabbit that was put into its cage, Pasteur had him tied down and then personally sucked the poisonous saliva out of its mouth into a glass tube so that it could be tested on the rabbit.

He eventually discovered an anti-rabies inoculation that was effective on animals, but he hesitated to test it on human beings. Then in 1885 a boy named Joseph Meister was brought to him after he had been bitten by a rabid dog and, after much doubt and self-questioning, Pasteur inoculated him. To his relief and delight the treatment was a success and the boy was cured. Years later he became the gatekeeper of the great Pasteur Institute that was built in Paris.

Since then many diseases and ailments have been alleviated or conquered as a result of the experiments carried out on laboratory animals. Diphtheria, typhoid, malaria and yellow fever have all been brought more or less under control by means of the scientific exploitation of animals, and more recently the fear of polio has been lifted from millions of people thanks to cultures grown in the kidney tissues of rhesus monkeys (*Macacus rhesus*). The wide and varied use made of animals is testified to by the fact that the very name guinea pig, one of the laboratory animals most frequently used, has come into the language to signify anyone who subjects himself to a trial of anything new.

The suffering caused by all this experimental work often seems inexcusable, but it cannot be denied that countless lives have been saved as a result of it. Sometimes, too, these lives have been saved eventually as a result of experiments that at the time seemed to laymen to be pointless and therefore needlessly cruel. Thus in 1889 two researchers tested the effect on animals of the complete removal of the pancreas. To the man in the street such work might have appeared to be of only academic interest, and the fact that all the animals developed diabetes and died would have provided added cause for condemnation. Nevertheless, this work became the basis of the years of research that led eventually to the virtual conquest of diabetes and has enabled the sufferers from it to lead normal lives.

Those concerned in them hope that some of the experiments being conducted in laboratories all over the world today will have similar happy outcomes. Recently many soldiers injured in the Korean and Vietnamese wars have benefited from inquiries made on dogs into shock and wound infections. Heart and lung machines to resuscitate the apparently dead have also been tried out on dogs. In one such research program at the Ukrainian Institute of Physiology in Kiev, a mongrel dog named Vesna was first drugged and then drowned. She was kept submerged for forty minutes, then taken out of the water, and the machine was switched on. After three minutes her heart began to beat again and then it was not long before her tail was wagging as happily as before the experiment began.

Another possibility for the future is what has been termed

"spare-part surgery." Various research programs at the present are devoted to the problem of keeping detached organs "alive" and then attaching them to a new host. Again, dogs are frequently the subject of these experiments, the results of which may well be blessed by many people in years to come, even though the details make horrifying reading. In one Russian experiment a Pomeranian dog was cut in two and its torso was then attached to one dog and its head to another. Such experiments made it possible to attempt the transfer of human hearts, and the first of these fantastic operations was carried out in South Africa in December 1967.

Of course, much of the current research is devoted to the cause and possible cure of cancer. Many thousands of animals are used every year for this purpose. The annual total of animals used in all medical research experiments must run into many millions, and the demands of the scientists are causing a great deal of concern to the conservationists. It is even causing concern to the scientists, though for the very different reason that if the animals they need become too severely depleted, their work will suffer.

According to a New York conference on the demands for live monkeys and apes for medical research, this concern is amply justified. Some staggering figures were presented. Since 1958 the total number of monkeys imported annually into America has ranged from 115,000 to 223,000, and it was estimated that for every monkey that arrived alive, two more died in capture or during transit. The majority of these monkeys were sacrificed to the demand for polio vaccine. The chief threat to chimpanzees comes from the new technique of kidney transplantation. The world population of chimpanzees has been put at about 250,000, and when it is realized that in the United States alone there are perhaps 30,000 people dying of kidney deterioration every year, it will be clearly seen that the wild stocks cannot long provide the number of animals needed for this work.

It is not only the medical laboratories that make such demands upon animal populations. Nowadays very large numbers of primates are used for research in anthropology and behavior. The number of gibbons in Thailand has been very seriously reduced because of the many hundreds used in anthropological studies, and it has been alleged that one American university buys eight thousand monkeys a year for behavior research.

Beside these figures the number of animals used in space research fades into insignificance, though this work naturally commands more public interest. The first animals to be so used were those put in an instrumented capsule developed for the nose cones of V2 and Aerobee rockets by scientists at the Wright Air Development Center in 1951. Later on in this series of experiments, white mice were photographed under conditions of weightlessness. Since then many animals have helped to pioneer man's leap into space. Even such un-likely-seeming creatures as water turtles have been involved. These were used in experiments on conditions of subgravity conducted at the National Institute of Aeronautics in Buenos Aires, Argentina, and a disconcerting aspect of the experiments was that the water containing the turtles would rise and float above the aquarium which then had to be lifted and fitted back around the water.

The animals most often used in space research, though, have been mice, dogs and monkeys. One of the first animal space travelers was an American squirrel monkey known as Monkey Baker, whose flight in 1959 was used to test such things as air supply and the effects of pressure and radiation. Other American animals that became quite well known for their space flights are Miss Patience, a four-pound monkey who helped medical teams to determine the effects of space on body chemistry, Sam and Miss Sam, two rhesus monkeys, and Ham, who was the first chimpanzee ever to ride in space.

Probably the most famous animal space traveler was Laika, the little husky sent up by the Russians in Sputnik II in November 1957. This flight ensured that Laika's name would figure in the history books, but it also meant that the dog was condemned to death, as there was then no means of bringing her back alive to earth. Because of this there was a world-wide howl of protest from animal lovers, but the Russians remained unrepentent. They revealed that Laika had undergone months of training to prepare for her ordeal and that she was conditioned to her strange cramped environment. She was fitted with a number of special instruments to record information about such things as respiration and heartbeat, and she was fed by another automatic device for the few days that she lived.

Animals remain of great value in space research and they are also now being used in quite another direction—in the exploration of the depths of the sea. Mice have been used to test the effects of pressure and have survived the enormous weight of water at depths of 3,000 and 4,000 feet. The mongrel dog Whiskey made a name for himself when he lived for twenty-three minutes without air in an experiment conducted at the New London Submarine Base. He breathed a saline solution saturated with oxygen and showed no ill effects for his adventure.

The sea and the life to be found within the sea is now beginning to play an important part in many research programs. Marine plants and animals are proving to be sources of many substances that promise exciting new medical developments. Already sea creatures have yielded chemicals that ease pain,

Miss Sam's test flight helped NASA medical teams to learn more about space effects.

fight viruses and inhibit the growth of tumors and act as stimulants upon the heart.

New heart drugs also seem a likely outcome of current research on the previously ill-famed kokoi frog of South America. The skin of this strange creature contains the strongest of all known poisons, now known to be ten times as deadly as that of the Japanese puffer fish, previously thought to be the most active venom on a poison per weight basis. There is no known antidote for the kokoi frog venom, which Cholo Indians have long used as an arrow poison, one frog producing enough venom for fifty arrows.

There seems to be no end to the possibilities of animal research. Even such bizarre creatures as fireflies, glowworms and sea plankton have proved to contain valuable secrets that can help man lead his increasingly complicated life. The cold light produced by these creatures, and also by bacteria and by microorganisms on fish, is what the scientists are studying. Already this cold light is being used in the United States to detect and identify air pollutants, and it is hoped to develop it to detect leaks of anesthetics in operating theaters, leaks from storage tanks containing toxic chemicals and even the drift of insecticides away from the intended target areas.

CHAPTER 8

FIGHT AGAINST CRUELTY

*

Despite the obvious benefits that have resulted from research on animals, there are people who remain very much opposed to it. They maintain that it is morally wrong to safeguard man's health at the cost of so much animal suffering and would very much like to see all laboratory experiments on animals forbidden by law. Some extremists are even convinced that doctors are guilty of an enormous confidence trick and that animal research has not won the advances claimed for it. This is a minority viewpoint, but a great many people have reservations about the use of laboratory animals. They condone the present situation because they would not like the opportunity of an advance in medical knowledge to be lost, but at the same time they feel that unnecessarily painful experiments should not be allowed. This point of view is not confined to members of the various antivivisection societies; it is shared by many of those who work in the laboratories. One nineteenth century scientist, Sir Charles Bell (1774–1842), even abandoned his work on the anatomy of the brain because he felt that to proceed further would have meant performing experiments that were altogether too unpleasant to be justified. Unfortunately, it is doubtful if scientists and laymen can ever reach agreement on what constitutes essential research and at what stage the experiments become unnecessarily and indefensibly painful.

For most of the nineteenth century there was no control at all, and it is true that some scientists then did behave in the unrestrained fashion antivivisectors apparently believe to be typical of research workers. Sentiment and morality were banished from their laboratories and vast numbers of animals were subjected to appalling torments. It almost seemed as if some of their experiments were deliberately designed to be as painful as possible.

One of the worst offenders in this respect was the French surgeon François Magendie, who was accused by some who watched his demonstrations of taking a positive pleasure in the pain he inflicted and of needlessly extending and repeating his tortures. To M. Magendie there was no element of cruelty in all this. To him the pain did not matter, for he believed it was an essential and important part of life. He even considered it wrong to use anesthetics for operations on human beings.

The majority of the experimenters, however, are, and always have been, responsible men with a deep regard for life, conscious of the pain they inflict and fully aware of the duty they owe to the animals they use. Also, in Britain at least, they are subject to the law of the land. The law controlling all experiments conducted in British laboratories dates from 1876, and the interesting thing is that it was to some extent the scientists themselves who agitated to bring it into force. A report that the training of veterinary students in France included operations on living and conscious horses first shocked them into action, and eventually a number of eminent scientists, including Darwin, Jenner, Owen and T. H. Huxley, signed a petition calling on the government to set up legal controls over animal experiments. A bill was introduced into Parliament on their behalf in 1875, but this clashed with one introduced a week earlier by Lyon Playfair for the R.S.P.C.A., and so a royal commission was set up to enquire into the subject. Both bills were withdrawn pending the findings of the commission, and then, after these were made known, the 1876 Cruelty to Animals Act was passed.

Under this act it became illegal to conduct painful experiments without the use of anesthetics, and if serious injury occurred during the course of the experiment, or if the animal was likely to suffer continued pain, then it had to be killed before it recovered consciousness. The conducting of experiments as a part of a lecture or demonstration to students was forbidden. The act was afterward weakened by the introduction of Home Office Certificates, whereby any of these restrictions could be evaded if shown to be necessary for the success of a particular experiment. Nevertheless, it gave a very real measure of protection to experimental animals, and continues to do so today. The need to extend this protection and bring it up to date is generally recognized, and in 1965 the government published a report proposing an increase in the number of inspectors and the registration of the breeders of laboratory animals.

Many countries, including Canada, New Zealand, France, Spain and the U.S.S.R., still give no legal protection to laboratory animals, and elsewhere the degree of protection varies enormously. The tiny state of Liechtenstein will not allow any use of experimental animals, and Denmark also has most stringent regulations under a law passed in 1953. Other countries, however, make little provision for inspection to make sure their laws are enforced.

In the United States the antivivisection movement began in 1883 with the founding of the American Anti-Vivisection Society, and now there are over two hundred societies in the movement, including five national ones. Their campaigning has been vigorous and sustained, and each biennium since 1897 laws against animal experimentation were introduced into Congress, though none were passed. The societies achieved more success in their efforts to abolish vivisection from public schools, for by 1945 six states had passed laws to that effect.

In 1945, too, bills to prohibit the use of animals for teaching and research purposes very nearly passed the legislatures of the states of New York and Massachusetts. This so alarmed the researchers that a counter organization, the National Society for Medical Research, was founded to put the facts about animal experimentation, from the experimenters' point of view, before the public. Supported by medical, dental, veterinary and research organizations, this society was so successful that by 1957 nine states and twenty-eight cities had passed laws making unclaimed animals from the public pounds available to approved research groups.

In the United States as elsewhere, the animal welfare movement is divided between those who work for the total abolition of experiments on animals and those who go no further than to say that these experiments should be properly controlled and unnecessary suffering and cruelty prevented. The National Anti-Vivisection Society takes the former viewpoint, and the American Humane Association, the latter.

The American Humane Association was the first national organization formed in the United States to fight against

A NAUSEATING JOB, BUT IT MUST BE DONE

President Theodore Roosevelt is the chief muckraker in this cartoon from the Utica Saturday Globe; *in 1906 meat-packing abuses led to legislation establishing federal inspection.*

cruelty to animals. It came into being at a meeting at Cleveland, Ohio, on October 9, 1877, adopted a constitution the following year and was incorporated under the laws of the District of Columbia on November 12, 1903. Its primary purpose was to prevent cruelty in the transportation of livestock, a subject which had been worrying humanitarians for some time and which, with the related question of cruelty in the way that animals were slaughtered, was to agitate them for a long while to come.

Even today the matter of abuses in the meat supply industry have not been completely resolved, but in the United States a great step forward was taken as far back as 1906, when Congress passed a law providing for federal inspection of the domestic meat supply. This was a reform forced upon the legislators by the activities of the humane associations and, more particularly, by the reception afforded to Upton Sinclair's novel *The Jungle*. Published in 1906, this book was a shocking revelation of the terrible conditions prevalent in the Chicago stockyards.

Federal regulation ensured that American standards of hygiene and quality would soar above what was general in the rest of the world. Conditions in the slaughterhouses of Britain, for example, remained bad even though agitation on this point had begun very much earlier. As far back as 1796 a writer was suggesting that legislation was necessary, and Sir Samuel Romilly (1757–1818) interested himself, unsuccessfully, in the humane slaughter of animals. Various Members of Parliament also tried to introduce legislation to protect animals and the first act of Parliament ever to recognize the rights of animals was passed in 1822 "to prevent the cruel and improper treatment of cattle."

It is hard to realize just how cruel and improper this treatment was. In those days the most callous abuse of animals was taken for granted. It was customary at the beginning of the nineteenth century to throw unwanted cats into the drains and, incredible as it sounds, many animals, including sheep, were customarily skinned alive. It was even quite commonplace for drovers to punish animals that gave them trouble by cutting off their hooves and forcing them to stagger along on their stumps. An early prosecution for cruelty in the United States in 1866 concerned a driver who, when his horses proved unable to pull a particularly heavy load of stones, put a heap of hay under them and set fire to it to "encourage" them. Similar behavior was several times reported in England. Allied to this general disregard of animal suffering was an aggressive sense of freedom, a robust hatred of official interference in private affairs, that added greatly to the difficulties of reformers.

In Britain the activities of the S.P.C.A. inspectors were

everywhere resisted. Many of the men were violently assaulted when they attempted to carry out their duties, and in 1838 one of them, an Inspector Piper, died after a particularly savage encounter at a cockfight. This popular sport had been outlawed by act of Parliament in 1835, but continued more or less surreptitiously in many parts of the country. The efforts of the S.P.C.A. to enforce the law had already resulted in a number of skirmishes and even pitched battles. When the society heard that there was to be a cockfight at Hanworth, in Middlesex, the secretary and two inspectors, one of them the unfortunate Inspector Piper, went down to intervene. Because violence was always probable at such an affair, they also enlisted two other men as assistants. The wisdom of going in strength was soon proved, for the inspectors were recognized on reaching Hanworth and the party was set upon by a group of infuriated "cockers." They fought their way clear of these assailants and, recruiting the aid of the village constable, moved on to the cockpit. By this time, however, tempers had become so dangerously inflamed that they were attacked even more ferociously than before. Sticks and staves were used freely, and it was only with the greatest difficulty that the inspectors and constable were able to fight their way back to the shelter of a nearby public house.

The mob might even have fought its way into this refuge if the uproar had not at that stage been interrupted by the arrival of a patrol of six men from Bow Street. The mob was broken up, seven of its ringleaders being arrested, and a surgeon was summoned to treat the wounds of the S.P.C.A. men. He found them all so badly injured that they could not at first be moved to London. Inspector Piper eventually had to be admitted to St. Thomas's Hospital, but nothing could be done for him and soon afterward he died. His attackers were lucky because he was found to be suffering from tuberculosis

Cock-fighting arouses fierce enthusiasm; in 1838 an attempt to stop a match caused a riot and the death of an S.P.C.A. inspector (cartoon by Florencio Molina Campos).

and this was declared to be the cause of death, but undoubtedly the beating he had received accelerated his end.

No one else had to sacrifice his life in the cause of protecting the animals of nineteenth century Britain, but a martyrdom of a lesser sort was demanded from the founder of the S.P.C.A., the Reverend Arthur Broome. In 1826 he suffered the indignity of being clapped into prison as a result of the society's having fallen into debt. The secretary, Lewis Gompertz, and Richard Martin organized a hasty collection among the supporters of the society in order to release him from this embarrassing confinement.

The society was not free from debt until 1828, and there was a shortage of money for a long time afterward. The lack of financial resources is clear indication of how little support there was for animal welfare work, for it shows that even the wealthier, more educated part of the population felt little sympathy for the cause. This is especially strange in view of the fact that many of these people treated their own horses scrupulously and lavished care and affection on household pets.

Indeed, pets were common throughout the country, in poor homes as well as rich, and had been for many centuries. Unfortunately, the habit of keeping pets seems to have played only a minor part in the developing of a conscience about cruelty to animals. Indeed, it is directly responsible for some of the cruelty, not only because of the savage whims of temper to which some of the pets are subjected, but also because many people are woefully ignorant of how to treat an animal and so are unintentionally cruel. The present concern of veterinary surgeons over the ill health and suffering caused to many pedigree dogs as a result of exaggerated fashions in breeding is another reminder that being kept as a pet does not always work only to the advantage of an animal.

The recurrent desire to improve on nature has also led to a great deal of pain being inflicted on horses. The Anglo-Saxons had the strange idea that they could help their horses to breathe more easily by slitting their nostrils, and it later also became customary to crop their ears by putting an iron shape to the ear and trimming off the excess flesh with a knife or scissors. Another peculiar fad was to cut off horses' tails, an operation known as docking. There was strong opposition to this fashion but, despite the efforts of reformers, it was only recently that it was forbidden by law.

Although this and most of the other legislation protecting animals from misuse is of such a recent vintage, there have, of course, always been individuals to whom the general cruelties have been abhorrent. Many of the Greek philosophers were outspoken on this subject and most of the higher philosophies and religions have included consideration for animals in their teaching. This has always been especially evident in Buddhism, a religion that demands a promise from its followers not to take the life of any living creature. Unfortunately, this can lead to a negative attitude whereby life is not taken but suffering is regarded with equanimity, but generally speaking this Buddhist teaching resulted in a standard of behavior toward animals superior to anything existing in the West until modern times.

It is unfortunately true that until comparatively recently there was reason for the Buddhist attitude that Christianity was the hell of animals. Compassion was the keystone of Christ's teaching, but his followers tended to forget that this was all-embracing and applied even to animals. For centuries virtually the only right that the Church allowed animals to retain was the bizarre one of being tried for crimes they were supposed to have committed. These animal trials seem utterly fantastic to modern ways of thought, but they were commonplace in the Middle Ages and large numbers of creatures were tortured to extract "confessions" and then executed.

The principal victims of this peculiar treatment were pigs. These ran unchecked through the streets of medieval towns, feeding on the plentiful supplies of garbage, and were much more akin to wild animals than to the domestic varieties of today. Attacks on human beings, especially children, were by no means unusual, and if one of these attacks had fatal consequences, the full majesty of the law was invoked against the offenders. A pig sentenced to death at Falaise in 1386 for killing a child was even dressed in human clothes and whipped through the streets before being beheaded.

It was possible too for animals not involved in the actual killing to be arrested as accomplices to the crime. This happened in 1370 in Burgundy, when three sows killed a boy and the entire herd was brought before the court. However, after listening to a powerful plea from the owner of the animals, the Duke of Burgundy decided that only the three sows should die, though he severely criticized the others for not having gone to the defense of the unfortunate boy. Similarly, in 1547 a sow and six piglets appeared in court at Sevigny charged with killing and eating a child, but although they were all found guilty, only the sow was executed, it being held that the young ones were not responsible for their actions as they had been led astray by their mother.

Whole populations of insects, rats and mice were sometimes brought to book for their crimes. Of course, in these cases judgments were impossible to execute and details of the trials make farcical reading, especially if the lawyer briefed to defend them was sufficiently ingenious. In 1521 the lawyer defending rats accused of destroying a barley crop argued that his clients could not be blamed for ignoring the summons to court since they were confined to their holes by fear of the "evilly disposed cats" of the plaintiffs. He said they would be prepared to come if given protection, and thought this could best be assured if the plaintiffs paid a large sum of money into the court, to be forfeited should any rats be molested by their cats. The court thought this a reasonable proposition, but the plaintiffs refused to put up the money and so the case was dismissed.

While awaiting trial, animals that were successfully arrested were put into jail like ordinary prisoners and were put to torture in order to wring confessions from them. The full repertoire of the rack and all the other instruments was brought into use, and the resulting screams and moans were interpreted as admission of guilt. When the sentence of death was passed, it was sometimes beheading, as in the case mentioned in Falaise, but was more often by hanging or burning. Creatures as large as bulls and horses and wolves were usually hanged, while cats and snakes were burned, being suspended over bonfires in baskets so that they should not escape.

Perhaps the most incredible thing of all regarding these animal trials is that they were not confined to the really antique, devil-ridden days but survived the Renaissance and lingered on into what is generally termed the Age of Reason. There were a number of these trials in the seventeenth century, including a case at Aix in 1694, when a horse was condemned to death by burning; and it was in this century, too, that a Canadian bishop excommunicated the wood pigeons in his diocese. At the beginning of the eighteenth century judgment was given in Brazil against some ants that had invaded the stores of a monastery, and as late as 1740 a cow was condemned to death in a French court.

In the second half of the eighteenth century the first suggestions of a need for a change in the general attitude to animals began to be made, but it was a long time before this was accepted generally. When an Oxfordshire clergyman, the Reverend James Grainger of Shiplake, was moved to preach in 1772 against the widespread cruelty to animals, the most charitable assumption his indignant parishioners could make was that he had gone out of his mind. Even the bishop became embroiled in the dispute that followed, and had to preach at Shiplake to make it plain that he supported the vicar. Such an episode made it very clear that the ideals of Christianity and the examples of such leaders as St. Francis of Assisi and St. Richard of Chichester had been very largely rejected by the bulk of the people who regarded themselves as Christians. They much preferred the Old Testament view that animals had been created only to satisfy man's needs and could be used as he wished.

As the eighteenth century passed, so a more humane spirit began gradually to make itself felt. The Reverend Mr.

Grainger was many years ahead of his parishioners in his abhorrence of cruelty, but when he preached that sermon, he was reflecting the views of many eminent thinkers of the day. Jeremy Bentham (1748–1832) was one of these who recognized the kinship existing between men and beasts, and in his *Introduction to the Principles of Morals and Legislation* he looked forward to the time when animals acquired those rights of which they had been for so long deprived.

This change in the general climate of opinion led some people to take more active steps to combat the cruelties with which they were surrounded. These reformers comprised a very small minority, but their efforts were significant and led eventually to the previously mentioned act of 1822. The first effort to organize these humanitarian impulses was made at Liverpool in 1809. A few interested people joined together to form the Society for the Suppression and Prevention of Wanton Cruelty to Animals, and although there was apparently not sufficient interest to keep this society active, it must take the credit for being the very first animal protection society. However, the honor of being the first effective organization in this field undoubtedly goes to the Society for the Prevention of Cruelty to Animals; it was founded in London in 1824 and the prefix royal was added in 1840.

Although it was a long time before this society was to win general support, its example was fairly soon followed elsewhere. Various subsidiary societies came into being in English towns and cities, and in the 1830s and 1840s it was extensively copied on the continent of Europe. The first German society was one started at Dresden in 1839, and within a few years others had sprung up in Germany and also in France and Austria.

The first American S.P.C.A. was founded in New York

in 1866 by Henry Bergh, and New York was the first state to pass laws for the prevention of cruelty to animals. By 1869 societies had also been founded in Massachusetts, Pennsylvania, New Jersey, Illinois, Minnesota and California. These states subsequently followed New York's example and enacted laws to protect animals, and since then legislation has continued until now there is no state or territory that is without some such provision.

In 1959, several years of work came to fruition when the American Humane Association and the R.S.P.C.A. jointly formed the International Society for the Protection of Animals to link the work of interested societies and individuals throughout the world.

CHAPTER 9

ZOOLOGY

THE GRADUALLY CHANGING climate of opinion that fostered the formation and eventual growth of these societies was partly the result of a tremendous upsurge of interest in natural history during the eighteenth and nineteenth centuries. Some of the credit for this belongs to the Swedish scientist Karl Linnaeus (1707–78), famous for the system of classification and description that he evolved for plants and animals. It was he who had the idea of giving every living thing two names; the first of these, the generic name, showing the family to which it belongs, and the second, the specific name, identifying its particular species. For example, all members of the dog family belong to the genus *Canis,* and this generic name is then followed by the name of the particular species. Thus, the wolf becomes *Canis lupus,* the fox is *Canis vulpes* and the domestic dog is *Canis canis.*

It might seem strange that a scientist so preoccupied with classification could have inspired a romantic interest in natural history and thus affect the humanitarian movement, but Linnaeus was a passionate lover of nature himself and he succeeded in infecting his followers with something of his own enthusiasm. This was especially so in England, where his example helped to make the new interest in nature study both fashionable and popular.

This led to the formation of natural history societies in every part of the country and to the publication of a new range of books about wild life. A great many scientists were involved in this activity, and some of the publications were of lasting zoological and biological importance, but by and large these lovers of natural history were amateurs and their work was of popular rather than scientific appeal.

One drawback was that the everyday language used and the lack, in some cases, of any sort of scientific background to help the naturalists evaluate their findings sometimes led to misinterpretation and the establishment of false ideas. Much of this was due to the common habit of assuming that animals acted according to a human scale of values. This is called anthropomorphism, and even when the writer of popular natural history did not always make this mistake, his readers frequently did.

A clear example of how mistaken this sort of interpretation can be was provided when the investigations of Eliot Howard in 1920 revealed the real impetus behind the song of the birds. For thousands of years men had listened to birds singing and had reasoned that such a cheerful and beautiful sound must be inspired by sheer joy. The truth proved much less poetic. It was found that the liquid notes were usually serving as a most unromantic "no trespassing" notice. When a male bird perches on a branch or fence and trills away, he is warning his rivals that the surrounding piece of ground is his territory and that he is prepared to defend it against intruders.

The apparently well-founded belief in the intelligence of beavers has also been shaken by critical examination. It had

Wild dog in Kruger National Park, genus Canis.

seemed that here was a case where the possession of reasoning powers could hardly be doubted, even when all possible
exaggerations had been removed from the tales told of the
animal. After all, the dams and lodges that it builds could
hardly be improved upon by human engineers. It has been
known to build up a mud platform to stand on when felling
trees and, when large logs have to be moved, it digs canals
to float them to the site of its dam.

However, modern scientists use a sound working rule,
known as "Lloyd-Morgan's canon," that an animal's behavior
should not be interpreted as the result of a high power of
mind if it can be satisfactorily explained as the outcome of
a lower. When the beaver's activities were reexamined in this
light, it became clear that much of its engineering ability
could be explained in terms of instinct and inborn patterns
of behavior rather than as the result of reasoning by the
individual.

The perfection of the dam is thus explained by the animal's

sensitivity to flowing water, which leads it to commence building in the middle of a stream and then to add fresh materials to the sides and the top. The curve and slope of the dam, so much admired for the perfection of design, would then appear quite naturally and without any conscious planning on the part of the beaver. The idea that beavers work by instinct rather than by applied intelligence is supported by reports of occasions when dams have been built or repaired unnecessarily and by the discovery that trees are felled haphazardly by round-the-trunk gnawing. It was previously believed that beavers understood the mechanics of tree felling and made the trunks drop just where they wanted.

Despite all the investigation necessary to produce this re-thinking about the beaver, it may well be that scientists have now retreated too far from the anthropomorphic view in denying the animal any awareness of what it is doing and why. Nevertheless, it is only sound common sense to be critical rather than credulous.

Despite the errors of anthropomorphism into which many eighteenth and nineteenth century naturalists were led, they deserve a great deal of credit for reintroducing the idea of making direct observations of living animals. This was a technique remarkably few zoologists had practiced since the far-off days of ancient Greece, when the science was, as it were, invented. Earlier civilizations had collected a certain amount of knowledge regarding animals, and in Egypt there was a vast amount of animal lore, but it was in Greece that deliberate investigations were first carried out and recorded along scientific lines.

The most notable of the early zoologists was undoubtedly Aristotle (384–322 B.C.). His work was of such basic importance that he is acknowledged as the founder of zoology. He was regarded as the ultimate biological authority for almost two thousand years, and his work and opinions are still frequently referred to.

His practical observations alone would be enough to earn Aristotle a place in any list of great naturalists, but he was not content merely to watch and note and experiment. He used the information he gathered as the basis of a series of deductions and theories that profoundly influenced the course of science. He gave a great deal of thought to the relationship between living things and devised a "ladder of nature," with inanimate matter at the bottom and man at the top, to show it.

It is strange that after this brilliant beginning zoology should then have languished so long, but for many long centuries the knowledge acquired by the Greeks was lost to all practical purposes, and even when it was rediscovered, the medieval mind was not equipped to continue the process of scientific advance. In the Middle Ages the world was considered to have definite limits in both space and time, and there was no conception of an infinity of knowledge. Since the world was limited, so was the number of facts that concerned it, and if enough time and energy could be devoted to the project, all these could be gathered together so that all knowledge would be revealed. Since there were no unfathomable secrets save God's will, research lost its savor and many agreed with St. Augustine on the unprofitability of enquiring into nature.

Even when there was a revival of interest in the scientific literature of the ancient world, the majority of the scholars were interested only in their texts and translations. Such men as Albertus Magnus (1206–80), who began to add a few personal observations to their commentaries, were very rare.

Almost the only medieval worker with a genuinely scientific

attitude was Frederick II (1194–1250), Holy Roman Emperor and king of Germany. He believed in observation and experiment and never hesitated to disagree with the recognized authorities, even Aristotle, when his own experiences contradicted their statements. In order to settle the speculation as to whether children brought up in isolation would speak Hebrew, he attempted unsuccessfully to raise some in the necessary silent and lonely fashion. It is also said that he had men cut open so that he could study their digestive processes. Luckily, most of his enquiries did not demand such drastic measures, though they all showed an equally practical and direct cast of mind. When he was told that in Egypt ostrich eggs were hatched by the sun, he immediately sent for some eggs so that the matter could be tested in Apulia. He also experimented with the artificial incubation of hens' eggs. In order to find out whether vultures relied more on sight than smell in discovering their food, he had the eyes of several birds sealed but left their nostrils open, and then had them released so that he could observe the success of their hunting.

Despite all this, the Emperor remained an isolated phenomenon, and zoology as a science did not really begin again until the sixteenth century, with the work of the Swiss naturalist Conrad Gesner (1516–65). He was a remarkable man, and his industry was phenomenal. Besides writing some ninety books, he kept up a voluminous correspondence with scientists all over Europe and generally performed many of the functions of present-day scientific journals. The text and illustrations of his work show he had made a close study of many of the creatures he described. He knew, for example, that the intruding cuckoo tipped the other young birds out of its foster-parents' nest, a discovery often credited to Dr. Jenner two hundred years later.

Further assistance in jerking naturalists out of their encyclopedic rut came from the astronomers, and especially from Galileo (1564–1642). The stars seem far removed from zoology, but once the old conception of the universe had been challenged and changed, all the sciences were freed from their strait jacket and able to begin vast moves forward. A definitive version of human knowledge was no longer possible, and so the idea of intensive and more narrowly directed research appeared. In other words, the change meant the end of the universal genius and the beginning of the specialized scientist.

Galileo had an immediate effect on zoology because he demonstrated that the new science of mechanics was as applicable to the study of living things as to everything else. Through it he was even able to explain why animals should be of such varying sizes and shapes and how it was that marine creatures were able to grow to be so much bulkier than those of the land. This information was eagerly seized upon by scientists, who abandoned their previous considerations of the psychic nature of animals and began to regard and investigate them solely as machines.

This was unfortunate for the animals because machines do not have feelings and so this attitude excused and encouraged the laboratory experiments that later became so numerous. It did, however, lead to a great increase in biological knowledge, for a galaxy of brilliant researchers was soon at work studying the anatomy and physiology of the animal and human body.

What could be achieved by this sort of research was demonstrated by the fantastic anatomical knowledge of Georges Cuvier (1769–1832), a Frenchman who became known as the "dictator of biology" and who really established the principle of the correlation of parts. This principle stems from

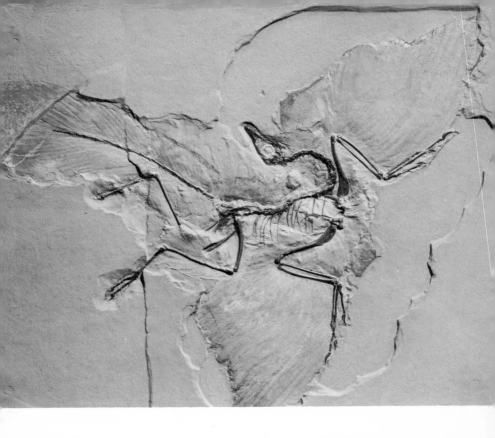

From the fossilized impression of a tailfeather (complete fossil above), scientists were able to reconstruct the Archaeopteryx (right), one of the world's first birds (Courtesy, American Museum of Natural History).

the fact that organs do not exist on their own but as parts of the whole body and their form depends on the way of life of the animal concerned. Carried to its logical extreme, this means that a single feather, if studied and interpreted with sufficient care and knowledge, could lead logically to the reconstruction of the whole bird. This sounds incredible, but the existence of *Archaeopteryx* was revealed originally by the discovery of the impression of a mere feather, and on one occasion Cuvier reconstructed an entire bird from one tiny piece of bone and had his work proved accurate by subsequent discoveries.

Meantime the finding and opening up of new lands multiplied the number of animal species known to the scientists. This necessitated a more logical system of classification and a standardized method of description. Scientific terminology looks ugly and sometimes seems to make a subject more difficult and boring but it eliminates possible errors of understanding and provides a useful form of shorthand. Without it, two zoologists might use the same word to describe completely different organs or creatures and it would be difficult, even impossible, to keep track of the work being done. It was easy to find a universal scientific language, for there was the common background of classical studies to draw upon, but for a long time the scientists remained overwhelmed by the mass of new material and an acceptable system of classification could not be devised.

Until the seventeenth century Aristotle's "ladder of nature" had to suffice, but he had worked at a time when there were only some five hundred known species, and a great many of the new creatures failed to fit into the categories he had created. The first big advance came when the English naturalist John Ray (1627–1705) began to arrange animals according to their physical features, such as toes and teeth and whether they had hearts with two or four chambers. His work helped to clear the way for Linnaeus, who, as has already been described, produced a system that for a long time offered a complete solution to the problem and which provided zoologists with an incalculably valuable tool.

Many workers were promptly jerked out of their absorption in anatomy and physiology and inspired with a new interest in the world of living animals. Some even took part in a sort of scientific goldrush to discover and name new species, and although much of this activity did not do much directly to advance scientific knowledge, it did give a tremendous impetus to zoological exploration. This was important not only for its own sake and because of the resulting advance in knowledge, but also for the enormous stimulation it gave to the popular and romantic interest in animals.

As always, it was the rare and the strange that provoked the interest, and people flocked to the traveling menageries and the newly opened zoos to see creatures they had previously known only as the subject of travelers' tales. It is possible that the reality was sometimes a bit of a disappointment, but there was always the hope that the next discovery would be truly sensational. Even Aristotle included a fair proportion of travelers' tales in his works, and later on the most unlikely stories and creatures were given credence by high and low alike. For example, in the Middle Ages it was generally accepted that in the north of Scotland there was a tree the fruits of which fell into the water where they became barnacles that later hatched into geese. A few skeptics, notably Frederick II of Germany, who sent north for some of the wonderful barnacles, derided such a belief, but other learned men saw no reason to doubt it. Sylvius, who later became Pope Pius II, visited Scotland in 1435 in the vain hope of witnessing the marvel, but was told that actually the tree grew farther to the north, in the Orkney Islands. John Gerard, whose *Herbal or History of Plants* appeared in 1597, cautiously admitted that he could not absolutely vouch for the accuracy of his description of this tree but gave unqualified evidence to the closely associated belief that certain geese did hatch from barnacle shells found on floating timbers. He referred his readers to the coast of Lancashire, where there was an island, known as the Pile of Flounders, on which the sea deposited large quantities of floating timber and other debris, even uprooted trees. A sort of froth appeared on these timbers and gradually hardened into barnacle shells, inside which the tiny goslings were formed.

Nineteenth century scientists were scornful of this general credulity but did little to correct it. In the early part of the century, zoologists had retreated into the museums again to sort out and classify and study the mass of material resulting from zoological explorations. Generally speaking, it was the amateur who remained inspired by a romantic love of nature, and even when one of these produced work of importance and value, the professional scientists often appeared reluctant to give it the attention it deserved. Sometimes, as with Charles Waterton (1782–1865), they had some excuse for this attitude. Waterton is nowadays valued for his observations of animal behavior and for his advanced understanding of the balance of nature, but he was so prejudiced against laboratory scientists, it is scarcely surprising that they preferred to take as little notice of him as possible. Also, he disliked Latin names and scientific terminology, so that to the scientist much of his work appeared confused and vague and practically unusable. In addition, he scandalized the hidebound with a succession of scientific practical jokes, such as when he manu-

factured a "missing link" from the skins of two howler
monkeys.

Although it is understandable that his more formal col-
leagues should object to these idiosyncrasies, it is a great pity
that more did not show their interest in natural history by
making observations of living animals instead of delighting in
the acquisition of museum specimens. It they had done so,
several species might have been saved from extinction. The
demand for specimens put a tremendous strain on some
depleted stocks, of birds particularly, and it has already been
mentioned that the last few survivors of the garefowl, or great
auk, were slaughtered by egg hunters in 1844. Again, when
what were thought to be the last nine elephant seals in
the northern hemisphere appeared off Guadalupe, scientists
rushed to secure specimens, heedless of the fact that they
might be the last living members of the species.

While these tragedies were taking place, many of the
disregarded romantic naturalists, appreciative of the pleasure
living animals could give and mindful of man's responsibilities,
were already advocating protective measures and the setting
up of sanctuaries. Charles Waterton was well in the van of
this movement, and as early as 1806 turned his Yorkshire
estate into a bird sanctuary. He was so far in advance of
contemporary thought that, to the amazement of everyone,
even his fellow nature lovers, he forbade his gamekeeper to
shoot the "beasts and birds of prey" that everyone else regarded as vermin.

CHAPTER 10

CONSERVATION

*

THERE HAD BEEN a few isolated attempts at conservation measures before the nineteenth century, but none were successful. In 1755 a Russian mining engineer named Peter Jakovlev had vainly petitioned the authorities in Kamchatka to halt the slaughter of the sea cow, and more than a hundred years before that the Bermuda Assembly had even legislated to protect the cahow, a bird sometimes called the Bermuda petrel, and the green turtle, but had failed in both instances.

It is not surprising that the Bermuda Assembly met with disappointment, for laws designed to protect animals can only be truly effective when they are reflecting the desires and attitudes of the public, and this was certainly not the case in the seventeenth century. It was not until the close of the nineteenth century that an influential section of opinion veered round to the support of the tiny band of naturalists trying desperately to make themselves heard on the need for animal protection and conservation.

The lack of public concern is made clear by the slowness of the American Audubon societies' climb to influence. The first of these societies, started in 1886, received such little support that it lasted only three years. The idea was later revived and a number of the societies were organized, but the members were generally mocked and regarded as collections of gullible and sentimental women and children.

Even by 1905, when they were incorporated nationally, the combined membership still represented only a pitifully small fragment of the population. When the societies sponsored prosecutions under such animal protection laws as did exist, they often had to be content with very hollow victories. Thus, in 1903, a man found guilty of killing a turkey hen out of season was fined one penny, and there were several similarly contemptuous judgments. It was a major achievement of the National Committee of Audubon Societies when enough money was raised in 1902 to provide four wardens to guard the nesting egrets of southern Florida. Three years later, one of these wardens, Guy M. Bradley, was shot and killed by a plume hunter. Not only that, but a local jury freed the man accused of the killing, declaring the evidence against him was insufficient. The first major victory in the battle against the plume hunters came in 1910, when the governor of New York signed a bill forbidding the sale of wild bird plumage in that state. Three years later a federal tariff act banned the importation of plumage, and the "feather fight" was virtually over.

The subsequent growth of the National Association, renamed the National Audubon Society in 1940, is a convincing proof of the change in public opinion. Now its wardens patrol something like a million acres of nesting and feeding grounds, giving protection to countless thousands of birds and animals. It organizes summer nature camps and wildlife tours, has a busy publications department and keeps numerous lecturers traveling the American continent with films of birds and wildlife generally. The Audubon Junior Club, started in 1910, also plays an important part in creating an awareness of conservation needs and ideals and has an enormous membership.

It might seem strange that the Audubon societies had such a long struggle to win public and government support, for the United States is the country that pioneered the idea of national parks and nature reserves. The world's first national park, two million acres at Yellowstone, was opened in 1872, fourteen years before the first attempt to found an Audubon society. Yellowstone, however, was not seen primarily as a wildlife refuge. It represented a determination to preserve a portion of unspoiled natural landscape and to provide a scenic pleasure ground "for the benefit and enjoyment of the people."

Of course, quite a bit of the enjoyment of the scene came from watching the animals that were part of it, and no doubt seeing these animals in their natural conditions helped to persuade many people that there was something to be said for conservation. This attitude was reflected in an act of 1894, giving protection to such animals as were to be found in the national parks, but otherwise there was little sign of any federal concern with conservation until Theodore Roosevelt (1858–1919) became President in 1901.

He was generally expected to show some interest in the subject, for he was keenly interested in animals both as a hunter and as a naturalist, but even the most optimistic conservationist had not expected such a flurry of activity. He was never too busy to listen to, and to support, anything designed to benefit North American wild life, and his presidency was marked by an improvement in the game laws and by the foundation of the wildlife refuge system.

Of course, it was not only in America that this more enlightened attitude gradually made itself felt. As early as 1884 President Kruger of the Transvaal had expressed regrets at the rapid disappearance of game animals from the Transvaal and had suggested that an animal sanctuary be put aside for their benefit. He continued to elaborate on this theme until eventually the Sabi Game Reserve was established in 1898.

Again, the move was in advance of public opinion, and real success did not come until 1923, when the South African Railways included the Sabi Reserve in its tours of places of interest and found, somewhat to its surprise, that to most people the view of the animals was the best part of the trip. Suddenly it was realized that "useless" animals had a commercial value, and a great deal of publicity and support was given to a revived plan for a national park. The necessary act was passed in 1926, and the Sabi Game Reserve became the Kruger National Park, fittingly renamed after the man who so many years previously had advocated protective measures for South Africa's wildlife.

In Canada, meanwhile, huge areas had been set aside as game reserves. The oldest of these is the Banff Park, dating from 1887, and the largest is the vast Wood Buffalo Park, sprawling over more than seventeen thousand square miles, in the neighborhood of the Great Slave Lake. Game reserves, sanctuaries and national parks also began to appear throughout Africa and in many parts of Asia. Many of these resulted from the efforts of the Society for the Preservation of the Wild Fauna of the Empire, renamed the Fauna Preservation Society. It was founded in December 1903, and since then has worked ceaselessly to save threatened species from destruction and to educate the general public to an awareness of its responsibility toward wildlife.

Since its formation, similar societies have come into being

Kruger National Park offers refuge to a variety of animals besides the wildebeests and zebras shown here.

in other countries, and in 1948 what is now known as the International Union for the Conservation of Nature and Natural Resources was set up to coordinate and supplement their efforts. One of the newer organizations is the World Wildlife Fund started in 1961 as a charitable foundation devoted to conservation. It aims to raise several million dollars a year for this work, and it has already accomplished a great deal. In an effort to interest younger people in this movement, the Wildlife Youth Service was started in May 1963, and two clubs—the Panda Club for those up to eleven years old and the Wildlife Rangers for those between eleven and eighteen —were organized. The idea is not only to inform and interest club members in matters relating to conservation, but to enable them to take an active part in various wildlife projects.

All this concern and activity might suggest that there is no longer any need to worry about the position of rare animals and that their survival is assured. Unfortunately, such is not the case. All too often these organizations are working against insuperable obstacles and against an opposition that is firmly entrenched and hostile to the idea of animal preservation. Even when there is no active opposition, animal populations concerned have sometimes declined to an almost hopeless level before protection measures can be taken. Many species have already vanished, despite all that could be done to save them, and the position of others is very insecure. It has been estimated that during the past fifty years at least seventy-five species of wild animals have become extinct.

Nevertheless, there are success stories to offset the discouragements. One of these comes from New Zealand and concerns the rediscovery of a bird, the *Notornis,* or takahe, long considered extinct. A doctor named G. B. Orbell became intrigued by the possibility that *Notornis* might still be in existence, and so collected all the available reports and rumors of possible sightings. He did more than this. He built a summer residence in the part of the backwoods where he thought the bird would most likely be found and devoted as much time as possible to the search. In 1948 he found what he was sure was the fresh footprint of a *Notornis,* but experts to whom he submitted the details declared that he was mistaken and that it was the track of a bittern or white heron. Undeterred by this skepticism, Dr. Orbell renewed his search and was rewarded almost immediately by the discovery of two living specimens of *Notornis* in the same area. He captured the birds but released them again as soon as he had taken a colored film to prove his claim.

The news of this earned headlines in the popular as well as the scientific press, and the New Zealand government promptly made the whole region into a reserve for the birds. These were given absolute protection, and heavy penalties were announced for anyone found in possession of the bird or its eggs.

Another of the brighter aspects of the conservation movement today is the frequent cooperation between nations, which sometimes completely transcends political boundaries and differences. Thus delegates from Canada, Denmark, Norway, the Soviet Union and the United States met in conference in Alaska in late 1965 to discuss the plight of the polar bear. The numbers of this animal have dropped considerably in recent years because many are being killed both by hunters in search of their profitable pelts and by sportsmen, some of whom have relied upon ski-equipped planes to eliminate the hardships and the dangers of their quest.

The conference came to the conclusion that although

there was little immediate fear of the polar bear becoming extinct, it was definitely in need of protection and should be treated as an international circumpolar resource. Unfortunately, a unified management policy was not immediately practicable owing to gaps in our knowledge of the animal's way of life. The Canadian Wildlife Service had started a five-year research project on the biology and ecology of the polar bear, but in the meantime it was thought best that each nation should take all necessary conservation action for itself and that there should be a full exchange of information by means of an international polar bear data sheet.

It is not only the large nations of the West that are setting the example in conservation. One of the most significant and heartening developments was the setting up by the Batawana tribe of Bechuanaland of their own wildlife reserve. These people live by hunting and seemed unlikely converts to game preservation. However, following a visit to the tribe's home in the Okavango Swamp in 1958, Mr. and Mrs. R. Kay started to fight for its fast-vanishing wildlife. They never tired of pointing out that unrestricted killing was as unwise for a hunter as it would be for a farmer to kill all the cows that would otherwise bear calves. Gradually the Batawana began to see the logic of the argument, and eventually about seven hundred square miles of the area's best hunting country were set aside as a game reserve. There remained the problem of raising enough money to ensure the success of the scheme, for poachers take notice of game guards rather than "no shooting" signs, but the decision itself was a tremendous step forward. The Moremi Wildlife Reserve, as it is called, has not been imposed upon the Batawana but it is something for which they had themselves seen the need.

So far, unfortunately, there has been little sign of this

new attitude spreading among Africans, and the outlook for much of the wildlife of the continent remains very bleak. The popular imagination still sees Africa as the big-game continent and visualizes vast herds wandering across the plains. The somber truth is that the game has already vanished from enormous stretches of country and the population of large animals is only a tenth of what it was at the beginning of the century.

Both white men and black men are responsible for this sad change. The early explorers and visitors found game in unimaginable numbers and responded by embarking on an orgy of slaughter for both pleasure and profit. Big-game hunters tried desperately to obtain records by outshooting each other and settlers saw the herds as an inexhaustible meat supply. In 1800 the quagga, a species of zebra, existed in South Africa in enormous herds many thousands strong, but was so relentlessly persecuted for its meat and its hide, from which shoes and even sacks for storing grain were made, that it was exterminated long before the end of the century. The very last specimen died in Amsterdam Zoo on September 12, 1883.

The surviving remnant of the game is still being murderously assailed, despite the cosy and comforting belief of many people that the animals left are safe in the national parks and reserves. Perhaps the chief threat to the survival prospects of many species comes from the native poachers, who work on a very different scale to the English countrymen who illegally take an occasional game bird or hare. In Africa the poachers account for hundreds of thousands of animals every year. Often muzzle-loaders, possibly with rusty nails as improvised ammunition, are fired into a herd, killing a handful of beasts but maiming many others and condemning them to a lingering and horrible death. Some victims die agonizingly from a

Each year large numbers of African giraffes are slaughtered by poachers who sell their tails as fly whisks.

variety of poisons, and others slowly strangle themselves in wire nooses. If an animal is caught by the leg in such a snare, its frantic efforts to free itself only cause the wire to cut deeper and deeper into its flesh, so that it suffers appalling pain until the poacher eventually arrives to kill it. In a struggle to escape from one such trap a rhinoceros found by game rangers had uprooted the tree to which the wire was attached but had almost severed its leg in the process.

One trapline found in Tanganyika extended for thirty miles, with a trap set at twenty-yard intervals. A large proportion of these contained animals, some dead but the majority slowly dying of hunger, exhaustion and pain. Elephants suffer severely from poaching, and the bodies of as many as twelve hundred of them have been found in one small area. Large numbers of giraffes die each year because their tails can be converted into fly whisks, selling at about 24 cents each.

Even if the poaching menace could be miraculously removed and everyone suddenly converted to the view that wild animals are not man's to destroy at will but represent something held in trust for the future, it will still become even harder in most places to preserve large populations of them, especially of the bigger species. This is because of the constantly increasing pressure of human population. At the moment there are some three billion people in the world, and by the end of the century there will most likely be at least twice as many. It is all too obvious that there will be little space to spare for wild animals. It is unfortunately already true that the demand for grazing and growing ground is resulting in a steady whittling away of national parks and game reserves.

It may well be that in the very near future all hope of saving some species in the wild will have to be abandoned, and then the zoos, condemned as they are by numbers of well-meaning but uninformed people who overestimate the animals' appreciation of freedom, will become their only home and their only hope of survival. Indeed, this stage has already been reached in some cases.

The milu, or Père David's deer, became extinct in its Chinese home in 1920, with the death of a solitary female that had somehow survived the slaughter of her few remaining companions at the beginning of the century. Fortunately, following the nineteenth century discovery of the animal, a few specimens had been sent to Europe and the eleventh

Duke of Bedford had managed to build up a small herd in his deer park at Woburn Abbey. He was eventually able to supply a number of zoos with stock, and it was only due to his efforts that the species survived.

The European bison provides another example of an animal that died out in the wild but was saved from extinction because of animals maintained in captivity in various zoos and parks. An International Society for the Protection of the European Bison was formed, and not only were small breeding stocks maintained at various centers in Europe, but in 1929 the species was reintroduced into Poland when five hundred acres of the Bialowieza Forest were fenced off to make an enclosure for them. Despite all this, the *Pedigree Book of European Bison,* published in 1932, listed only thirty animals as purebred. Since then the numbers have built up and there are now several hundred European bison in zoos and zoo parks throughout Europe and Russia, and even a few in the United States. The climax of this success story came in 1956, when a group of the animals living in the Bialowieza Forest enclosure was released to complete freedom in the forest. The results so far suggest that the bison will be successfully returned to the wild.

Success is not certain because this involves a lot more than merely raising enough of the animals and then turning them loose. They have to be helped over the transition period while they lose the traits and habits acquired during their semi-domestication, and there are a great many factors, such as the ratio of males to females, to be considered. If the released animals are to thrive and breed, they must make up a natural group, and the full requirements of such a group are not always very clear.

Observations in the wild and work at such establishments as Whipsnade have, however, provided a great deal of infor-

Orangutans in Sarawak are being reaccustomed to life in the wild.

mation on this subject of natural groups, which affects all social animals, that is, the ones that live together in herds and flocks. With deer, for example, the hinds have to out-number the stags before normal behavior and rutting will occur.

Another point to be watched with groups of animals in the wild is that they do not become overprotected to the extent that they become too numerous to maintain a healthy stock. This happened fairly recently with the hippopotamus in Uganda's Queen Elizabeth National Park. A survey in 1959 showed that the hippo numbered about fifteen thousand, which was far too many, so that there was serious overgrazing and erosion. This, in return, affected the animals themselves, and many adults were found to be weighing as much as a thousand pounds less than normal.

At the risk of offending those people who regarded the sanctuary as a place where nature was not to interfered with, it was decided that the hippos would have to be thinned out. At the moment about a thousand a year are cropped, being shot at night and the meat sold the next morning to eager local buyers. It is claimed that this supplies the annual protein requirements of nearly forty thousand Africans. In this way everybody, including the remaining hippopotamus population, benefits.

Cropping wild animals in this way probably offers the best way of selling the idea of conservation in some areas. It is certainly becoming more and more evident that conservation is not merely a matter of forbidding the killing of certain animals or of shutting them up in a marked-off stretch of the country and leaving them to it. Despite the idea of noninterference, it is sometimes necessary for man to step in to make sure that one species does not do too well at the expense of others. It therefore becomes obvious that ideal conservation methods demand a much better and more detailed understanding of animals' lives than is at present possessed. To this end a great deal of research is being carried out into all aspects of animal behavior. Typical of this is the project being conducted at the Bako National Park in Sarawak to see if young orangutans can be reaccustomed to living in the wild. The experiment began in November 1961 with three young animals, and has been very successful. The apes were gradually weaned from utter dependence on their human friends and adapted themselves to a life of complete freedom. They have been kept under close observation all the time, and so a great deal has been learned about the behavior of a species that had previously remained somewhat mysterious because of the difficulty of studying it under natural conditions.

CHAPTER 11

HABITS AND HABITATS

Similarly intensive studies of various other species have already added greatly to the store of knowledge about animal behavior, and many of the popular notions regarding the lives of wild animals have been proved completely wrong. One of these is the idea many people still cling to, that animals live in a state of bloodthirsty anarchy. Instead, their lives are governed by a complexity of laws and instincts, all of which help to ensure the survival of the species. Because of this, predators, the carnivores that prey on the other beasts, are by no means the villains they were formerly thought to be. They have a much more difficult time than is sometimes realized and by and large have to be content with a diet of the very old, the very young or the unfit. The American zoologist Chris Crisler has observed that caribou have a built-in speed advantage over the wolves that prey on them and that even healthy calves are able to outstrip their pursuers. The animals pulled down are the sick and decrepit, and this selective killing is actually beneficial to the caribou population.

Not only are these northern wolves necessary to preserve a

natural balance, but study of them reveals very different creatures to the eerie, ravening gray beasts of the adventure stories. During their stay in the Arctic Mr. and Mrs. Crisler reared a number of wolf cubs and found them to be gentle and fascinating companions. Of course, other people had previously reared wolf cubs as pets and had commented on their amenability, but the Crislers were not working in the confines of a zoo or of a cage in a garden. They were interested in the natural life of their animals, and they remained on friendly terms with them after the wolves had matured and were leading the normal life of their kind, hunting and killing their prey.

One of the most attractive things about the wolves was the genuine affection they showed for each other and for the second lot of cubs reared by Mr. and Mrs. Crisler. The cubs paid special attention to the male wolf, possibly because normally he is the one who does most of the hunting and brings home tidbits, but both adult animals worked hard to care for them. It was found that they brought back food, often from long distances, in their stomachs. They apparently possess some means of halting or controlling the processes of digestion while doing this, for when it was regurgitated the meat was always red and fresh-looking.

Serious fights between pack members are rare. Usually the submission signal (described on page 23) brings things to a halt when one of the combatants has had enough. This observance of ritual is especially valuable for such powerful animals as wolves. If it did not exist, there would be a great deal of unnecessary and wasteful slaughter among the pack as the animals established their places in the social hierarchy. Its place in society, or rank, means more to an animal than it does to the most class conscious of human beings. Those at the top of the list, first in order of dominance, feed first when a kill has been made, and they retain their superior status in all the activities of the group.

This system of dominance first came to the notice of zoologists when a Norwegian scientist, T. Schjelderup-Ebbe, began to study the social structure of a flock of hens he kept and discovered that in all the squabbles witnessed between pairs of hens one bird pecked and the other submitted. He kept careful note of all this activity and soon found that there was a definite pecking order, or system of dominance. Each bird knew its place in the order and did not attempt to peck at one which stood higher in the hierarchy.

Since then, careful observation has revealed that this idea of dominance is common to almost all animal societies. To some extent the pattern revealed is simple and has obvious advantages. The members of a group soon discovered which of their fellow members they must fear and which they can dominate and, with the acceptance of those positions, tensions within the group are minimized and a stable society is ensured. It is also favorable to the survival and even improvement of the species, since the finest specimens within the group are assured of first choice of food, territories and mates and so have the best chance of passing on their qualities to future generations. Indeed, in some societies only the most dominant of the males have the opportunity of passing on their genetic inheritance. This has been clearly demonstrated by studies of the sage grouse, a chickenlike bird living in the western United States. The males go through an elaborate ritual of display and threatening behavior in order to establish dominance during the mating season, and a handful of the birds, about 1 per cent of the total male population, establish themselves as master cocks. Although they make up such a small fraction of the population, these master cocks will do as much as 80 per cent of the mating.

In many cases, however, the advantages of dominance are not so apparent. Even in societies such as herds of cows, where status brings no advantages whatsoever, it is still eagerly pursued. In some other animal societies the regard for position and status has become exaggerated to such an extent that it constitutes a threat to the species rather than an aid to its preservation. This can be seen with lions. They have a rigid system of dominance and woe betide any maturing animal who attempts to usurp any of the privileges of the adult members of the pride. A great many young lions, more than the species can afford, are killed every year because their ambitions outrun their discretion.

Another cause of serious lion mortality is the fighting that often takes place to defend or secure hunting territories. A sense of territory is very strongly developed in a great many creatures, although it was not recognized until 1920, when the English ornithologist Eliot Howard published his book *Territory in Bird Life*. His studies had made it clear to him that the supposed incessant struggle for mates was the result of assumption and faulty observation, and that the real competition was for territory. The male bird that secured an exclusive territory was then assured of a mate. This revolutionary theory was accepted, but at first it was thought to apply only to birds. Then an increasing number of observations by field naturalists made it clear that most of the rest of animal creation was just as property conscious.

The place regarded as home varies from the couple of yards of beach claimed by a fiddler crab to the enormous circular areas, perhaps as much as a hundred miles in circumference, of a wolf pack, but whatever its size, it is a necessity of life and is zealously guarded. In many cases only a token defense is called for, since there appears to be a generally appreciated natural law that the occupant of a territory should be the victor in any dispute concerning it. Thus territorial defense is often more of a matter of sound and fury than of flying fur and feathers.

This is certainly the case with the South American howler monkey. When two groups spot each other, the forest is transformed into bedlam as they each leap insanely through the branches at the edge of their own territory and shriek frenzied defiance and rage at each other. After a spell of this, each group is able to withdraw, feeling, one imagines, thoroughly satisfied and convinced that the intruders have been put firmly in their place.

Dr. C. R. Carpenter, an American zoologist who spent eight months in the 1930s studying howler monkeys on Barro Colorado Island, Panama, recorded that although adjacent groups lived in this state of constant hostility, actual invasions were very rare and, when they did occur, always ended in defeat for the invaders. In another of his protracted and intensive studies of primate behavior, this time of rhesus monkeys on Santiago Island, off Puerto Rico, Dr. Carpenter did encounter the unusual phenomenon of territorial conquest and was able to analyze the situation and discover the cause. He found that the group responsible for the upsetting of the natural law contained an individual of such extraordinary dominance that he was able to imbue his group with his own confidence and spirit and inspire them to flout normal territorial observances. When the leader was removed, the group lost its domination over its neighbors and retired to a blameless life on its own patch of the island.

These same rhesus monkeys had given a very clear indica-

The flickering tongue of the
snake helps it to track its prey.

tion of the vital importance of territories by their behavior on the journey from India to Santiago Island. There were, of course, no territories on board ship, and without this stabilizing influence rhesus monkey society fell apart. Anarchical conditions prevailed, and these were made worse by the policy of keeping them short of food, which, it was thought, would make them more readily adaptable to the different diet available in their new home. Group and family obligations alike were completely forgotten as they scrambled for the rations provided. The old notion of "jungle law" was realized to the full on that voyage, and a number of the young monkeys died as a result. When they reached Santiago Island, it took a year for them to reorganize themselves into groups and territories. During that year, when there was no need to struggle for food since an ample supply was provided daily, most of the infant mortality was the result of rough treatment at the hands of adults.

This incident not only emphasizes the importance of territories but serves as a reminder that much of animal behavior can be studied only in the wild. The social organization and other factors influencing behavior can seldom be reproduced in zoos, and so studies of captive animals kept in zoos are sometimes influenced and distorted by the unnatural lives they lead. Where the indoor research worker comes into his own, however, is in the investigation of the physiological and psychological bases of behavior. This work is sometimes able to explain why an animal acts in the way the field naturalist has observed, and so provides some sort of picture of the different worlds animals inhabit.

Just how different the physical world appears to various creatures is something that is not always realized. Few animals, for instance, see the world in the same colors as we do. The apes are nearest to us in this respect, but most mammals, including dogs, appear to see everything in varying shades of gray. They are compensated for this by having other senses developed beyond anything known in human beings. Their hearing is often both very much keener than that of men and also covers a greater range of sounds. That is why dogs are able to respond to the so-called silent dog whistles that emit a note too high for the whistler to hear. Again, smell is much more important to dogs, and many other creatures, than sight. Not only can dogs pick up scents that are utterly imperceptible to human beings, but they can even distinguish the separate components of a smell mixture.

Snakes seem to be able to taste smells. At least, they track their prey by making use of what is known as Jacobsen's organ, which is situated in the roof of the mouth. The flickering tongue of the snake picks up tiny particles from the air or ground and conveys them to this organ, where the taste or the smell is identified. In addition to this, some species of snakes are extremely sensitive to heat, or rather to the presence of a warm-blooded animal. Sensory pits on their heads are activated by the warmth given out by other animals and so the snakes are able to turn and attack immediately, without having to wait for the animal to come in sight.

A very long list could be made of these exceptionally acute or strange senses. It would include the ability of flies and butterflies to taste with their feet, the way in which the consciousness of altered water pressures enables fish to avoid rocks and other obstacles and would raise questions about the unimaginable world lived in by the bees, who, although insensitive to red, are able to see the ultraviolet color that is invisible to human beings and are also able to detect polarized light. However, despite the length of such a list it would be far from exhaustive, for man is only just beginning to find out about the sorts of worlds inhabited by the other creatures that live on this earth.

He is only just beginning to find out some of the answers to the many queries raised through the ages about animals' intelligence and their possession of reasoning powers. For a long time such abilities were generally much exaggerated and all animal behavior was interpreted in human terms. Then, at the beginning of the twentieth century, there was a tremendous reaction against this attitude. Anthropomorphism, as it is called, became the cardinal sin of observation and, not content with that, the new generation of scientists denied the animals both thought and emotion. Their lives were reduced to the mechanical reaction to stimuli, and mind consequently returned to being the glorious prerogative of man.

The careful laboratory work of this behaviorist school undoubtedly advanced the knowledge of zoologists and biologists much more rapidly and certainly than the interpretations of the previous centuries, but it now seems likely that the reaction went too far.

Many experiments have shown that nearly all animals, even the lowliest and, consequently, the most dependent on instinct, have the ability to learn by experience and to adapt their behavior accordingly. This is true even of a one-celled animal such as a stentor, a funnel-shaped protozoan. In a famous experiment a stream of carmine particles was directed at a stentor, which at first attempted to evade and blow away the unwanted and objectionable food and then withdrew into its protective tube. When it came out again half a minute later, the carmine attack was recommenced and the stentor immediately contracted into its tube without wasting time with ineffective evasive action. It clearly possessed sufficient consciousness to remember the response called for by that particular situation.

In the higher animals this ability to learn is enormously increased, and with many species it is so noticeable and plays such an important part in the lives of individuals that to the ordinary observer they appear to be guided as much by intelligence as by instinct. It has to be remembered, however, that intelligence is a word without any precise and universally accepted meaning. It can be used to describe what is merely an ability to learn from experience and to avoid past mistakes, or it can be reserved for behavior that demands a genuine understanding of a situation. The vast majority of animal actions that are usually described as intelligent fall into the first category. This is true even of performing and working animals, most, if not all of which, go through their repertoires only because they have learned that to do so is a way of gaining a reward or avoiding punishment. They do not necessarily have any understanding of what they are doing. Thus dogs have been found able to open latched gates not because they understand the principle of the latch but because a series of trial and error attempts has gradually associated a particular action with the desired result.

Some experiments, however, have made it impossible to doubt that some animals do possess a certain amount of reasoning ability, or insight. There is some disagreement as to how many animals have reached this degree of mental development, but it certainly cannot be completely denied to the apes and monkeys.

One of the earliest experimenters to prove their ability to solve complex problems was Wolfgang Koehler, a German psychologist who in 1913 began a series of observations on the ape colony maintained in the Canary Islands by the Prussian

Academy of Science. He was the first to demonstrate the utilization by apes of sticks and boxes in order to secure food that had been put out of their reach. One of his chimpanzees even fitted two bamboo rods together in order to make a rake long enough to reach the food. Many other experiments have since confirmed these findings, and sticks have been used not only as rakes, but have also been thrown at food suspended out of reach and used to knock it down. Jojo, a chimpanzee at the Yerkes Laboratories of Primate Biology, learned to put a short pointed stick into the hollow end of a larger stick and to use the whole as a spear to reach food that was otherwise unobtainable. Even more remarkable, there have been instances of apparent cooperation. When a box of food, with a rope attached, proved too heavy for one young chimpanzee to pull in singlehanded, he apparently signaled to a companion to help him and then they both pulled on the rope and secured the prize.

This story raises the question of communication between animals and, as a natural corollary, of communication between animals and men, something that has fascinated mankind for thousands of years. One of the chief arguments used by animal psychologists for denying animals the ability to think is that their lack of language makes it impossible for them to form mental concepts, even of such things as "mate" or "home." The reasoning of the apes and monkeys already mentioned thus becomes a matter of visualization, of seeing what has to be done and doing it, rather than of conscious, abstract thought. It is said that if they were able to form concepts, they would have words for the things concerned, but that all animal language expresses only emotion and is never indicative. The vocal repertoire of apes has been closely studied, and although these animals have quite a wide range of meaningful sounds, it has been found that this does not correspond to a human language. One ape was kept isolated from any contact with its fellows for the first five years of its life but was still as proficient in ape language as if it had been reared amidst the clan. The sounds it made were obviously instinctive and were expressions of mood rather than actual words.

Since there is no ape language that man may learn, attempts have been made to solve the problems of communication by the reverse process, by teaching apes to speak human language. A great deal of time and effort has gone into this, but so far it has not been very rewarding. Dr. Keith Hayes and his wife probably came nearest to success when they brought up a chimpanzee named Vicky as if she were their own child. They even manipulated her lips to help her produce recognizable sounds, and in six years she came nearer to genuine speech than had ever previously been the case with any animal. She could manage a small number of words, including "mama," "papa," and "cup," and would use the last one of these to indicate that she was thirsty and wanted a glass of water.

CHAPTER 12

COMMUNICATION

*

BECAUSE WE RELY so much on speech, it may be that we place too much importance on this ability and are too quick to assume that a lack of words implies a lack of reasoning power and makes subtle communication impossible. Although animals have such a limited vocabulary, and the cleverest of dogs is usually considered capable of recognizing only about a hundred words, they may achieve an almost equally effective means of communication by more subtle methods. The honey bees have no vocalized language, but researchers have shown that they are nevertheless able to convey to each other a great deal of precise and detailed information. How they managed this was discovered by the German scientist K. von Frisch. He found that the returning bee performed what he called a "waggle dance" to show the other members of the hive the whereabouts of the food source and how far it was away from the hive. The dance comprises a figure-eight movement, and it is the number of turns made that tells the watching bees how far they will have to fly. The longer the distance, the fewer the turns made, and, working with a stopwatch, Von

Frisch found that when the food was at a distance of about 656 feet, there would be about 8 turns made in 15 seconds. When the distance increased to 984 feet, only 6 turns were made. The two loops of the figure eight are joined by a straight run during which the abdomen is waggled from side to side, and it is this bit of the dance that shows the direction to be taken. If the bee moves upward, it means the food lies in the same direction as the sun, and if it moves downward, the food is away from the sun. The precise angle at which it lies from the hive is shown by the angle at which the dancing bee holds its head. All this means that bees are able to communicate abstract facts to each other, something that used to be considered the prerogative of man, and the scientists found this so startling that at first they hesitated to accept Von Frisch's findings. However, they were soon checked and corroborated by other workers, and are now generally accepted. Details of the dancing of the bees appear in all modern books on animal behavior. There can, therefore, be no disputing that at least one creature has developed a system of communication without words.

One does not need to go to the insects for proof of the comparative unimportance of words. Most animals are capable of picking up and interpreting nuances of expression and behavior that are completely missed by human beings, and anyone who has ever kept a dog knows how quickly it is aware of an intended walk. Sometimes this awareness by an animal of its owner's intentions is so obvious and so quick that in their search for explanations the nonscientists have been provoked into speculations regarding telepathy and similar forms of psychic intercommunication.

The publicity given to the "thinking" and "talking" animals that are in the news from time to time has encouraged

*The honey bee performs an elaborate dance
to show his hive where to find food.*

some people to accept these fantastic ideas. Possibly the most
famous of these animals was a horse named Clever Hans. He
belonged to an elderly German named Wilhelm von Osten,
who was convinced that animals were genuinely intelligent.
In order to prove this, he spent a great deal of time trying to
teach various specimens to count and calculate. In 1896 he
came into possession of the young Russian stallion that was
to become world famous as Clever Hans, and this horse
apparently quickly mastered the mysteries of addition, sub-
traction, multiplication and division. Stories of his abilities
spread, and were received with wonder by some and with a
great deal of skepticism by many others. However, no one
could see how the trick, if trick it was, was worked, and in
1904 a scientific commitee appointed to investigate Clever
Hans and Von Osten's claims, had to admit that there was

no evidence of fraud. Despite this, many people remained unwilling to concede that a horse could possess such powers, and a second commission of inquiry was organized.

Included on the new panel was a man named Oscar Pfungst, a psychologist who was already a convinced skeptic regarding Clever Hans, and he soon discovered that there was no question of the horse being able to calculate or to show any unusual degree of understanding. What was happening was merely a demonstration of the animal's acute powers of observation. When he was asked a question, Hans started pawing at the ground and kept a wary eye on his master. Von Osten was naturally rather tense during the questioning, but insensibly relaxed when the horse reached the right answer, and this, so far as Hans was concerned, meant that it was time to stop "counting." There was no conscious or deliberate fraud involved, but when a screen was put up between the horse and its master, Hans lost all signs of cleverness.

The belief that it is possible to talk to animals was revived and received a great deal of publicity early in 1962 when Lord Dowding assured his fellow members of the House of Lords that rats or other household pests would obey a spoken request to leave a place they were infesting. The peers, and the newspaper readers, were amused by the idea of the Air Chief Marshall and his wife politely asking mice and silverfish to leave their house, but a great deal of genuine curiosity was aroused. Mr. Allen Boone, an American author whose book had provoked Lord Dowding's comments in the House of Lords, described the method as the mental equivalent of shaking hands, and many people who tried it agreed, in great surprise, that it worked.

One suggested explanation for this was that the voices

possessed some subtle tonal quality affecting animals, a theory which would seem to go a long way toward explaining other remarkable successes that some people have with them. One of the things which it might explain is the horseman's word, a charm which was supposed to give its possessor power over all horses. Anyone who knew the word was believed to be able to exert the most complete control over any horse and to make it savage or calm at will. The charm was obviously a valuable asset in the days when horses played an all-important part in daily life, and its possession was the jealously guarded secret of a few grooms and blacksmiths and other men who had to do with the animals. One of the most famous of those who were reputed to know the secret of the word was the American horse tamer John S. Rarey (1827–66).

He came to England in 1858, and soon earned an extraordinary reputation for the way he could handle and subdue even the most vicious of animals. His handling of Cruiser, a stallion previously regarded as absolutely unmanageable, was especially marveled at. This horse had killed three men, and even its keeper, the only man it would allow to approach it, regarded it with trepidation and always carried a stout cudgel. The atmosphere must have been tense when Rarey stepped into the enclosed stable yard alone and unarmed, for those watching were probably convinced he would be savagely attacked and would need to be rescued. At first it seemed as if these fears would be realized. Cruiser was enraged at the sight of the intruder and charged him furiously. But then came the great surprise. When the stallion was almost on top of him, Rarey was seen to say something and Cruiser stopped in his tracks. It stood there, trembling but with all the fire and the savagery suddenly gone, and not only allowed the tamer to approach but even submitted to stroking and caresses. Rarey never claimed to possess the horseman's word, but this was only one of several occasions on which he appeared to calm a horse and establish an understanding with it by the use of some indistinguishable word or phrase.

It is possible that the secret of the horseman's word is linked in some way to the system of "talking to animals" that has been described by Mrs. Barbara Woodhouse. This consists of blowing up and down noses to establish confidence and friendship, and its efficacy has been testified to by many other animal lovers. Mrs. Woodhouse was even able to use it to calm, and subsequently to control, a steer that had been maddened by ill treatment in a cattle market, a feat reminiscent of the taming of Cruiser, and it has been said that gypsies used the same method to forge a link between themselves and their horses, and that once this was done they were even able to control the animals from a distance.

These abilities are remarkable enough, but such a communion is not quite the same thing as talking to animals. Nor has the fact that scientists have been able to assign meanings to some of the sounds made by some creatures helped much. It is true that Dr. Konrad Lorenz has so mastered the jackdaw language that he is able to instruct his birds to fly away or to fly back home, but this is still not conversation. Genuine conversation has to be a two-way process, and this would seem to be an unlikely happening between man and beast.

Some scientists are convinced, however, that talking with animals is feasible, and expensive and far-reaching research is being conducted to turn the dream into a reality. Dr. John Lilly, the man most involved in this work, has eliminated dogs and other pets and even chimpanzees as possiblities and has concentrated his attention on the more alien-seeming dolphin. In his book *Man and Dolphin,* published in 1962, he explained that this is largely because the size of the dolphin's brain is favorable to the attempt.

The friendliness of dolphins has been remarked upon for centuries and by people of widely varying cultures. The ancient Greeks and Romans told a great many stories of how the creatures attended upon ships, helped shipwrecked sailors to the shore and occasionally frequented bathing resorts to be made pets of by the inhabitants. For a long time these stories were either ignored or laughed at, but it is now realized that they rested on a basis of fact.

The first "friendly dolphin" of modern times was Pelorus Jack, who became famous in the late nineteenth century because of the way in which he regularly piloted ships through Cook Strait, New Zealand. He kept to this self appointed task for over a quarter of a century, and the New Zealanders became so fond of him that in 1911 they accorded him protection by a special Government Order in Council. His disappearance, and presumed death, was well publicized and widely mourned. Forty years later another New Zealand dolphin brought world-wide fame to the North Island fishing village of Opononi when it made friends with bathers there and even allowed children to ride on its back. Its accidental drowning after it became wedged between rocks plunged Opononi into gloom, and not merely because of the economic effects on the town. People were genuinely moved and women and children wept when they were told that their dolphin friend was dead.

Some of the stories about dolphins suggest a more purposeful friendship than the New Zealand specimens showed. Indian and South American fishermen claim that they actively cooperate with them and drive fish into their nets. They so value this partnership that one Indian fisherman even took a competitor to court, charging that he had enticed away the plaintiff's dolphin assistant and persuaded it to drive the fish into his nets instead.

Indirect support for this belief in the dolphins' willingness to cooperate with man can be found in the amazing story of the whalers of Eden, in Australia, who for nearly a hundred years carried on their work in close collaboration with a herd of killer whales. These creatures (*Orcinus orca*) are closely related to the dolphins, but, unlike them, have seldom been credited with friendly feelings toward anything. Instead, they have been generally reviled as the fiercest and most blood-thirstily savage creatures in the seas, hence their name.

One of the very few groups of people to credit them with any redeeming features was the Tlingit tribe of North American Indians. The ancient stories of this people explained that the killer whale was created because a wood carver of the Seal People Band decided that it would make the Indians happy if such a creature existed. He accordingly carved the first killer whale out of yellow cedar wood and put it into the water with its head pointing up the inlet. He then told it to hunt the other water creatures for its food but never to hurt a human being. He told it that when it appeared in the bays, the Indians would ask it for food and it was then to drive the seals and the fish in toward the land to make it easy for the men to catch them. The Tlingits claimed that the killers had always obeyed this command and regularly aided them in their fishing. This sounds unlikely, but it cannot be denied that the killer whales of Eden worked with the local whalers like a fantastic pack of trained dogs. In the winter the killers

*Tales of "friendly dolphins" have been common through-
out history, and scientists today are adding facts to folklore
(Marineland of Florida).*

lurked in wait for the migrating whales that passed by the coast and would try to harry their quarry into the bay, fitting their actions intelligently to those of their human allies in the boats. If the whalers were not about when the killers spotted a target off the coast, the main body of the pack would attack the herd while a smaller section hurried into the bay and gamboled about in the water until they were seen and the longboats were launched.

The herd of killer whales dwindled over the years, and the last survivor, known as Tom to the whalers, who could recognize individual killers and had their own names for them, died in 1930. Appropriately enough, his body was washed into the bay and his skeleton is still preserved in Eden. The whalers concerned in this strangest of enterprises always insisted that the killers had some means of communicating with each other over a distance, and Dr. Lilly accepts the possibility of this. He is certain that their relations the dolphins have a language of their own.

The noises they make have been noted for many centuries. The Greek poet Oppian, writing in the second century A.D., described how dolphins would bark as they chased the mullet, and in recent years Marine Studios in Florida have even issued a gramophone record of dolphin noises. The officials of these modern oceanaria, and scientists who come into contact with the animals, are sure that many of these sounds have specific meanings and are much more precise than the instinctive cries of monkeys and apes. Dr. Lilly even found that the dolphins he was experimenting on were imitating the human voices that they heard. When tape recordings were analyzed, words and phrases could be easily identified, although there was apparently no discernible pattern of selection evident. Perhaps the most remarkable of all the incidents described by Dr. Lilly, and the one which probably holds out the greatest hope for the success of his efforts to establish interspecies communication, concerned a dolphin that reversed the procedure and conducted an experiment on the experimenters. This happened in 1958 when the animal was being taught to whistle, one of the noises commonly made by these creatures, in order to obtain a reward. Dr. Lilly noticed that each successive whistle was being raised in pitch, and this continued until the frequency became too high for human hearing, although the movement of the dolphin's blowhole showed that the animal was still whistling. Dr. Lilly stopped giving the reward once he could no longer hear the whistle, and after a couple or more tries the dolphin lowered the pitch to within what it had discovered to be the limits of human hearing.

If it does become possible to communicate with dolphins, or with any other animals, the effect on man himself will be incalculable. Very early man had no reason to see himself as something superior to the rest of creation. Although he might fear and hate them, he could still feel a kinship with the wild beasts that surrounded him. However, human inventiveness and the discovery that some animals could be enslaved soon changed that, and for thousands of years now man has seen himself as something apart and godlike. This attitude has engendered contempt for the animal creation which has in turn made it possible for society to accept and condone much pointless slaughter of animals and the infliction upon them of intolerable cruelties. Even people who would never be consciously cruel to animals have often been guilty of treating them as living toys and playthings.

Nevertheless, in recent years more and more people have begun to grope their way toward the realization that the world was not given solely to man to exploit as he pleases. Such people have already accepted that man is a part of nature and not something apart from and superior to it, and if it ever did become possible to talk with dolphins, this truth would become unavoidably evident to everyone. Man would have reverted, in fact, to something like the attitude of early man. There would be one great difference, however. Ancient man was aware of his inferiority in the face of the teeth and talons of the wild beasts that surrounded him, but modern man controls power that makes even the strongest animal puny and ineffective. It is to be hoped that by the time man is able to speak with dolphins or other animals, he has grown up sufficiently to accept the members of another intelligent species as friends and not as potential rivals and enemies. Otherwise it is only too likely that the discovery of the dolphins' potentialities might be the signal for some fanatic to preach that they should be destroyed before they become a threat to human superiority.

INDEX

*